Florida's B.E.S.T.
Standards for MATH

Geometry
with *CalcChat®* and *CalcView®*

B.E.S.T. Test Prep and Practice Workbook

- Review & Refresh

- Self-Assessments

- B.E.S.T. Test Prep

- Post-Course Test

- Correlation to Florida's B.E.S.T. Standards

- Evidence-Based Scale Worksheets

Big Ideas Learning™

Erie, Pennsylvania

Big Ideas Learning and *Big Ideas Math* are registered trademarks of Larson Texts, Inc.

Printed in the United States

ISBN 13: 978-1-63736-238-9

456789—25 24 23 22

Contents

H means the entire section is honors. H means that the section contains honors content.

Contents

(H) means the entire section is honors. (H) means that the section contains honors content.

Contents

(H) means the entire section is honors. (H) means that the section contains honors content.

Contents

H means the entire section is honors. **H** means that the section contains honors content.

Contents

(H) means the entire section is honors. (H) means that the section contains honors content.

Contents

H means the entire section is honors. **H** means that the section contains honors content.

Contents

Evidence-Based Scale Worksheets

About the B.E.S.T. Test Prep and Practice Workbook

Review & Refresh

Use the Review & Refresh exercises to practice the key concepts taught in each section as well as practice prior skills to improve retention.

Self-Assessments

Use the self-assessments provided for every section and chapter to rate your understanding of the learning targets and success criteria.

B.E.S.T. Test Prep

Use the cumulative test provided for each chapter to prepare for standardized test questions, including multiple choice, multi-select, gridded response, and fill-in-the-blank.

Post-Course Test

Use the Post-Course Test to measure your understanding of all content within this course. This assessment is designed to prepare you for standardized test questions, including multiple choice, multi-select, gridded response, and fill-in-the-blank.

Correlation to Florida's B.E.S.T. Standards

Use the correlation to see the standard(s) addressed by each item in the B.E.S.T. Test Prep and Post-Course Test.

Evidence-Based Scale Worksheets

Use the Evidence-Based Scale Worksheets to monitor your learning of Florida's B.E.S.T. Standards. Each worksheet focuses on one benchmark, and is broken down into four leveled targets, or mini-goals, to help you measure whether you have achieved the learning.

1.1 Review & Refresh

1. Determine which of the lines, if any, are parallel or perpendicular. Explain.
   Line a passes through $(-2, 0)$ and $(1, 6)$.
   Line b passes through $(-3, 5)$ and $(3, 1)$.
   Line c passes through $(1, 1)$ and $(4, 7)$.

2. Solve $4 + x = 15$.

3. A robot vacuum cleans at a constant speed of 4 feet per second. It will travel 600 feet, plus or minus 40 feet. Write and solve an equation to find the minimum and maximum numbers of seconds it cleans.

4. Evaluate $\sqrt[3]{27^2}$.

5. Graph $f(x) = \dfrac{1}{2}x - 4$ and $g(x) = f(x + 2)$. Describe the transformation from the graph of f to the graph of g.

In Exercises 6–9, use the diagram.

6. Name two lines.

7. Name three collinear points.

8. Give two names for the plane.

9. Name two line segments.

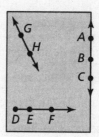

1.1 Review & Refresh (continued)

10. Use zeros to graph $y = x(x - 1)(x + 3)$.

11. Organize the results in a two-way table. Include the marginal frequencies.

You conduct a survey that asks 32 students in your class whether they have pets or siblings. The results show that 21 of the students surveyed have siblings, 13 have pets, and 4 have no siblings or pets.

1.1 Self-Assessment

Use the scale to rate your understanding of the learning target and the success criteria.

| 1 | I do not understand yet. | 2 | I can do it with help. | 3 | I can do it on my own. | 4 | I can teach someone else. |

	Rating	Date
1.1 Points, Lines, and Planes		
Learning Target: Use defined terms and undefined terms.	1　2　3　4	
I can describe a point, a line, and a plane.	1　2　3　4	
I can define and name segments and rays.	1　2　3　4	
I can sketch intersections of lines and planes.	1　2　3　4	

1.2 Review & Refresh

In Exercises 1 and 2, solve the equation.

1. $-4 + y = 1$

2. $-7x = 28$

3. Write an inequality that represents the graph.

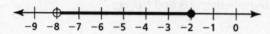

4. Use intercepts to graph the linear equation $-2x + 4y = 16$. Label the points corresponding to the intercepts.

5. Determine whether the relation is a function. Explain.

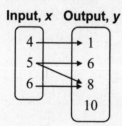

6. Graph $f(x) = 4 - 2^x$. Identify the asymptote. Find the domain and range of f.

Florida Geometry
B.E.S.T. Test Prep and Practice Workbook

1.2 Review & Refresh (continued)

7. Find *BC*.

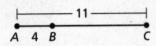

8. Plot the points in a coordinate plane. Then determine whether $\overline{AB}$ and $\overline{CD}$ are congruent.

$A(-3, 7), B(-3, -1), C(1, -3), D(1, 5)$

9. Sketch the figure described: plane *A* and plane *B* intersecting at line ℓ.

1.2 Self-Assessment

Use the scale to rate your understanding of the learning target and the success criteria.

| 1 | I do not understand yet. | 2 | I can do it with help. | 3 | I can do it on my own. | 4 | I can teach someone else. |

	Rating	Date
1.2 Measuring and Constructing Segments		
Learning Target: Measure and construct line segments.	1 2 3 4	
I can measure a line segment.	1 2 3 4	
I can copy a line segment.	1 2 3 4	
I can explain and use the Segment Addition Postulate.	1 2 3 4	

1.3 Review & Refresh

In Exercises 1 and 2, find the perimeter and area of the figure.

1.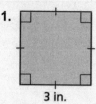

3 in.

2.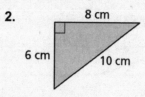

8 cm

6 cm

10 cm

In Exercises 3 and 4, solve the inequality. Graph the solution.

3. $a + 3 < 7$

4. $\dfrac{z}{6} \geq 1$

5. Identify the segment bisector of $\overline{AB}$. Then find $\overline{AB}$.

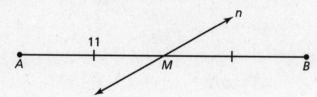

6. The endpoints of $\overline{CD}$ are $C(-2, 4)$ and $D(4, -4)$. Find the coordinates of the midpoint M. Then find CD.

7. Solve the literal equation $18x + 3y = 6$ for y.

In Exercises 8 and 9, factor the polynomial.

8. $7z^2 - 21z$

9. $81x^2 - 25$

Name _____ Date _____

10. Name two pairs of opposite rays in the diagram.

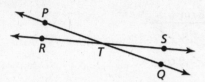

11. Simplify $\dfrac{d^{-3}d^{11}}{d^7}$. Write your answer using only positive exponents.

12. The function $p(x) = 50 - 2x$ represents the number of party favors remaining after x guests are served. How many favors remain after 5 guests are served?

13. Find AC.

A   3   B   12   C

1.3 Self-Assessment

Use the scale to rate your understanding of the learning target and the success criteria.

| 1 | I do not understand yet. | 2 | I can do it with help. | 3 | I can do it on my own. | 4 | I can teach someone else. |

	Rating	Date
1.3 Using Midpoint and Distance Formulas		
Learning Target: Find midpoints and lengths of segments.	1 2 3 4	
I can find lengths of segments.	1 2 3 4	
I can construct a segment bisector.	1 2 3 4	
I can find the weighted average of two or more points on a number line.	1 2 3 4	
I can find the midpoint of a segment.	1 2 3 4	

1.4 Review & Refresh

1. Does the table represent a linear or nonlinear function? Explain.

x	−2	−1	0	1	2
y	1	4	7	10	13

In Exercises 2 and 3, solve the equation.

2. $x + 2 = 2x - 8$

3. $\dfrac{x + 1}{2} = -3$

4. Give another name for $\overline{CD}$.

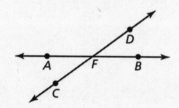

5. The endpoints of a segment are $J(-2, 3)$ and $K(-4, -1)$. Find the coordinates of the midpoint M and the length of the segment.

6. You deposit $100 into a savings account that earns 3% annual interest compounded monthly. Write a function that represents the balance y (in dollars) after t years.

7. Graph $g(x) = |x + 2| - 1$. Then describe the transformations from the graph of $f(x) = |x|$ to the graph of g.

In Exercises 9 and 10, consider rectangle *ABCD* with vertices $A(1, 3), B(1, 5), C(6, 3),$ **and** $D(6, 5)$.

8. Find the perimeter.

9. Find the area.

1.4 **Self-Assessment**

Use the scale to rate your understanding of the learning target and the success criteria.

| 1 | I do not understand yet. | 2 | I can do it with help. | 3 | I can do it on my own. | 4 | I can teach someone else. |

	Rating	Date
1.4 Perimeter and Area in the Coordinate Plane		
Learning Target: Find perimeters and areas of polygons in the coordinate plane.	1 2 3 4	
I can classify and describe polygons.	1 2 3 4	
I can find perimeters of polygons in the coordinate plane.	1 2 3 4	
I can find areas of polygons in the coordinate plane.	1 2 3 4	

1.5 Review & Refresh

1. Find the perimeter and the area of $\triangle ABC$ with vertices $A(-2, 2)$, $B(-2, -5)$, and $C(3, 2)$.

2. Solve $2(x - 3) + 1 = 5$.

3. Simplify $\sqrt{18}$.

4. The positions of three pillars are shown. Cords connect Pillar A to Pillar B and Pillar B to Pillar C. Which cord is longer? About how far is Pillar A from Pillar C?

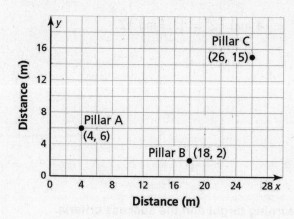

5. Graph $y \geq -x + 1$ in a coordinate plane.

1.5 **Review & Refresh** (continued)

6. $\overrightarrow{KM}$ bisects $\angle JKS$. Find $m\angle JKS$.

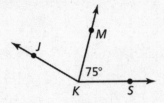

7. $\overrightarrow{BD}$ bisects $\angle ABC$. $m\angle ABD = 47°$. Find $m\angle DBC$ and $m\angle ABC$.

8. Point Y is between points X and Z on $\overline{XZ}$. $XY = 14$ and $YZ = 18$. Find XZ.

1.5 **Self-Assessment**

Use the scale to rate your understanding of the learning target and the success criteria.

| 1 | I do not understand yet. | 2 | I can do it with help. | 3 | I can do it on my own. | 4 | I can teach someone else. |

	Rating	Date
1.5 Measuring and Constructing Angles		
Learning Target: Measure, construct, and describe angles.	1 2 3 4	
I can measure and classify angles.	1 2 3 4	
I can construct congruent angles.	1 2 3 4	
I can find angle measures.	1 2 3 4	
I can construct an angle bisector.	1 2 3 4	

Name_____ Date_____

1.6 Review & Refresh

1. Find the area of $\square ABCD$ with vertices $A(1, 2)$, $B(3, 6)$, $C(7, 6)$, and $D(5, 2)$.

2. The midpoint of $\overline{JK}$ is $M(1, 3)$. One endpoint is $K(5, 4)$. Find the coordinates of endpoint J.

3. Identify the segment bisector of $\overline{DF}$. Then find DF.

```
     3x − 1      5x − 9
  •——————+——————•——————+——————•
  D           E           F
```

4. Solve $|z - 4| = 1$. Graph the solution.

5. Find the product of $(x + 2)$ and $(3x - 1)$.

6. The total cost (in dollars) of renting a karaoke room for x hours is represented by the function $f(x) = 10x + 10$. The hourly rate is increased by 50%. The new total cost is represented by the function $g(x) = f\left(\frac{3}{2}x\right)$. Describe the transformation from the graph of f to the graph of g.

1.6   **Review & Refresh** (continued)

7. Given $m\angle EFG = 62°$, find $m\angle EFH$ and $m\angle HFG$.

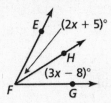

8. $\angle 1$ is a complement of $\angle 2$, and $m\angle 2 = 42°$. Find $m\angle 1$.

9. $\angle 3$ and $\angle 4$ are supplementary, and $m\angle 3 = 105°$. Find $m\angle 4$.

1.6   **Self-Assessment**

Use the scale to rate your understanding of the learning target and the success criteria.

| **1** | I do not understand yet. | **2** | I can do it with help. | **3** | I can do it on my own. | **4** | I can teach someone else. |

	Rating	Date
1.6 Describing Pairs of Angles		
Learning Target: Identify and use pairs of angles.	1 2 3 4	
I can identify complementary and supplementary angles.	1 2 3 4	
I can identify linear pairs and vertical angles.	1 2 3 4	
I can find angle measures in pairs of angles.	1 2 3 4	

Name_____ Date_____

Chapter Self-Assessment

Use the scale to rate your understanding of the learning target and the success criteria.

1 I do not understand yet.　**2** I can do it with help.　**3** I can do it on my own.　**4** I can teach someone else.

	Rating	Date
Chapter 1 Basics of Geometry		
Learning Target: Understand basics of geometry.	1　2　3　4	
I can name points, lines, and planes.	1　2　3　4	
I can measure segments and angles.	1　2　3　4	
I can use formulas in the coordinate plane.	1　2　3　4	
I can construct segments and angles.	1　2　3　4	
1.1 Points, Lines, and Planes		
Learning Target: Use defined terms and undefined terms.	1　2　3　4	
I can describe a point, a line, and a plane.	1　2　3　4	
I can define and name segments and rays.	1　2　3　4	
I can sketch intersections of lines and planes.	1　2　3　4	
1.2 Measuring and Constructing Segments		
Learning Target: Measure and construct line segments.	1　2　3　4	
I can measure a line segment.	1　2　3　4	
I can copy a line segment.	1　2　3　4	
I can explain and use the Segment Addition Postulate.	1　2　3　4	
1.3 Using Midpoint and Distance Formulas		
Learning Target: Find midpoints and lengths of segments.	1　2　3　4	
I can find lengths of segments.	1　2　3　4	
I can construct a segment bisector.	1　2　3　4	
I can find the weighted average of two or more points on a number line.	1　2　3　4	
I can find the midpoint of a segment.	1　2　3　4	

Chapter 1
Chapter Self-Assessment (continued)

	Rating	Date
1.4 Perimeter and Area in the Coordinate Plane		
Learning Target: Find perimeters and areas of polygons in the coordinate plane.	1 2 3 4	
I can classify and describe polygons.	1 2 3 4	
I can find perimeters of polygons in the coordinate plane.	1 2 3 4	
I can find areas of polygons in the coordinate plane.	1 2 3 4	
1.5 Measuring and Constructing Angles		
Learning Target: Measure, construct, and describe angles.	1 2 3 4	
I can measure and classify angles.	1 2 3 4	
I can construct congruent angles.	1 2 3 4	
I can find angle measures.	1 2 3 4	
I can construct an angle bisector.	1 2 3 4	
1.6 Describing Pairs of Angles		
Learning Target: Identify and use pairs of angles.	1 2 3 4	
I can identify complementary and supplementary angles.	1 2 3 4	
I can identify linear pairs and vertical angles.	1 2 3 4	
I can find angle measures in pairs of angles.	1 2 3 4	

Chapter 1

B.E.S.T. Test Prep

1. Select all the expressions that are greater than $\left|-2\right|$.

   Ⓐ 0

   Ⓑ $\left|-2.1\right|$

   Ⓒ $\left|-0.5 \bullet 4\right|$

   Ⓓ $\left|-1.9\right|$

   Ⓔ $-\left|4\right|+\left|-8\right|$

2. What is the common ratio of the sequence $2, -4, 8, -16, 32, \ldots$?

   Ⓐ -6

   Ⓑ -2

   Ⓒ $-\dfrac{1}{2}$

   Ⓓ $\dfrac{1}{2}$

   Ⓔ $\dfrac{1}{6}$

3. For which set of points is $\overline{AB} \cong \overline{CD}$?

   Ⓐ $A(-2, 1)$, $B(-2, 5)$, $C(1, -4)$, $D(1, 3)$

   Ⓑ $A(0, 3)$, $B(4, 2)$, $C(0, 5)$, $D(4, 3)$

   Ⓒ $A(0, 2)$, $B(0, 1)$, $C(4, 1)$, $D(5, 2)$

   Ⓓ $A(-1, -4)$, $B(4, -4)$, $C(-3, -6)$, $D(-3, -1)$

4. Evaluate $h(x) = 6.1 - 3.4x$ when $x = -2$.

5. Find the distance, in units, from $(0, 0)$ to $(3, 4)$.

Chapter 1 **B.E.S.T. Test Prep** (continued)

6. Find the area of the polygon.

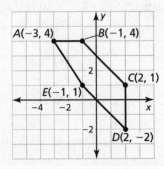

Ⓐ 9 square units

Ⓑ 12 square units

Ⓒ 17 square units

Ⓓ 24 square units

7. Which square root is in simplest form?

Ⓐ $\sqrt{9}$

Ⓑ $\sqrt{8}$

Ⓒ $\sqrt{30}$

Ⓓ $\sqrt{48}$

8. What is the solution of $|x - 5| \leq 2$?

Ⓐ $3 \leq x \leq 7$

Ⓑ $-3 \leq x \leq 7$

Ⓒ $x \leq 3$ or $x \geq 7$

Ⓓ $x \leq -7$ or $x \geq 3$

9. What is the solution of the system $2x - y = 4$ and $3x - 2y = 2$?

Ⓐ $(3, 2)$

Ⓑ $(6, 8)$

Ⓒ $(10, 14)$

Ⓓ $(0, -1)$

10. The ratio of the measure of an angle to the measure of its complement is 2 : 3. What are the two angle measures?

Ⓐ 30° and 45°

Ⓑ 30° and 60°

Ⓒ 36° and 54°

Ⓓ 72° and 108°

11. An object is launched from the top of a hill and travels in a parabolic path until it reaches the ground. Write a quadratic function that models the path of the object with a maximum height of 200 feet, represented by a vertex of $(25, 200)$, landing at the point $(55, 0)$.

_____

Chapter 1

B.E.S.T. Test Prep (continued)

12. Which equation is written in point-slope form?

(A) $y - 2 = 3(x - 3)$

(B) $y + 1 = 2x + 5$

(C) $y = -3x + 4$

(D) $y = -7$

13. The endpoints of $\overline{AB}$ are $A(2, 5)$ and $B(-4, 7)$. Find the coordinates of the midpoint.

(A) $(3, -1)$

(B) $(-2, 12)$

(C) $(-1, 6)$

(D) $(3, 6)$

14. Select all the points that are collinear with points Q and T.

(A) X

(B) S

(C) R

(D) W

(E) V

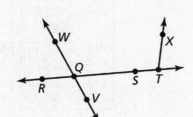

15. What is the domain of the function $y = 5\sqrt{6 - 2x}$?

(A) $x \leq 3$

(B) $x < 3$

(C) $x > 3$

(D) $x \geq 3$

16. Which data set has the least median?

(A) 0, 2, 3, 3, 0, 1

(B) 1, 2, 5, 5, 6, 0, 0

(C) 0, 0, 5, 6, 5, 0, 5

(D) 7, 0, 9, 9, 1, 1

17. Find the measure of $\angle LNK$. Then classify the angle as *acute*, *right*, or *obtuse*.

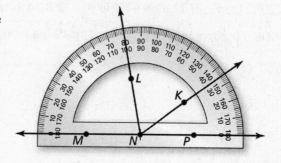

Chapter 1

B.E.S.T. Test Prep (continued)

18. $\angle 1$ and $\angle 5$ are vertical angles, $\angle 5$ and $\angle 6$ are supplementary angles, and $m\angle 6 = 110.2°$. What is $m\angle 1$, in degrees?

19. The electric current I (in amperes) an appliance uses is given by $I = \sqrt{\dfrac{P}{R}}$, where P is the power (in watts) and R is the resistance (in ohms). Find when $I = 5$ amperes and $R = 4$ ohms.

20. A container in the shape of a rectangular prism has a volume of 1080 cubic inches. What are the dimensions of the container?

(A) $\ell = 18$ in., $w = 180$ in., $h = 188$ in.

(B) $\ell = 18$ in., $w = 12.8$ in., $h = 16.8$ in.

(C) $\ell = 18$ in., $w = 6$ in., $h = 10$ in.

(D) $\ell = 18$ in., $w = 10$ in., $h = 14$ in.

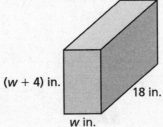

$(w + 4)$ in.   18 in.

w in.

21. $\angle BCA$ and $\angle ACD$ form a linear pair. $\angle BCA$ is represented by $(2x - 5)°$ and $\angle ACD$ is represented by $(3x + 10)°$. What is $m\angle ACD$?

(A) $35°$

(B) $61°$

(C) $65°$

(D) $115°$

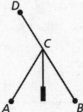

Name_____ Date_____

2.1 Review & Refresh

1. Approximate $\sqrt{21}$ to the nearest (a) integer and (b) tenth.

2. Determine whether the graph represents a function. Explain.

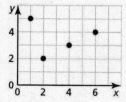

3. Describe the transformation from the graph of $f(x) = -x + 2$ to the graph of $g(x) = 2f(x)$.

4. Two angles form a linear pair. The measure of one angle is nineteen times the measure of the other angle. Find the measure of each angle.

5. Find the perimeter and the area of $\triangle ABC$ with vertices $A(1, 2)$, $B(1, 6)$, and $C(3, 4)$.

6. The distance from one asteroid to another is 1.876×10^6 kilometers. Write this number in standard form.

7. In the diagram, $\overrightarrow{DB}$ bisects $\angle ADC$, and $m\angle ADB = 56°$. Find $m\angle CDB$ and $m\angle ADC$.

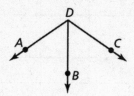

2.1 Review & Refresh (continued)

8. Find $(3m^2 - 8) - (2m^2 + 5m)$.

9. Write an inequality that represents the graph.

10. Let p be "you post a video" and let q be "your video goes viral."

    a. Write the conditional statement $p \rightarrow q$.

    b. Write the converse $q \rightarrow p$.

    c. Write the inverse $\sim p \rightarrow \sim q$.

    d. Write the contrapositive $\sim q \rightarrow \sim p$.

2.1 Self-Assessment

Use the scale to rate your understanding of the learning target and the success criteria.

| 1 | I do not understand yet. | 2 | I can do it with help. | 3 | I can do it on my own. | 4 | I can teach someone else. |

	Rating	Date
2.1 Conditional Statements		
Learning Target: Understand and write conditional statements.	1 2 3 4	
I can identify the hypothesis and conclusion of a statement.	1 2 3 4	
I can write conditional statements and their related conditional statements.	1 2 3 4	
I can write biconditional statements.	1 2 3 4	

2.2 Review & Refresh

1. Identify the hypothesis and the conclusion. Then rewrite the conditional statement in if-then form.

   Fracking causes microearthquakes.

2. Classify the polygon by the number of sides. Tell whether it is *convex* or *concave*.

3. Write a recursive rule for the sequence.

n	1	2	3	4
a_n	25	21	17	13

4. Write an equation of the line that passes through the points $(2, 2)$ and $(0, 4)$.

5. Determine whether the equation $y = 2x^2$ represents a *linear* or *nonlinear* function.

6. Graph $g(x) = 4x^2$. Compare the graph to the graph of $f(x) = x^2$.

2.2   Review & Refresh (continued)

7. Find $\left(3p^2 + p - 1\right) + \left(2p^2 - p - 3\right)$.

8. Solve $7^{2x+3} = 7^{13}$.

9. Write the next three terms of the arithmetic sequence $2, 5, 8, 11, \ldots$.

10. Solve the equation $3x - 4 = -2x + 6$.

11. Use the Law of Detachment to determine what you can conclude from the given information, if possible.

If the temperature is below 15°F, then you will wear gloves. You wear gloves.

2.2   Self-Assessment

Use the scale to rate your understanding of the learning target and the success criteria.

1	I do not understand yet.	2	I can do it with help.	3	I can do it on my own.	4	I can teach someone else.

	Rating	Date
2.2 Inductive and Deductive Reasoning		
Learning Target: Use inductive and deductive reasoning.	1 2 3 4	
I can use inductive reasoning to make conjectures.	1 2 3 4	
I can use deductive reasoning to verify conjectures.	1 2 3 4	
I can distinguish between inductive and deductive reasoning.	1 2 3 4	

2.3   Review & Refresh

1. Find a counterexample to show that the conjecture is false.

   If a quadrilateral is convex, then it is a square.

In Exercises 2 and 3, solve the equation. Justify each step.

2. $z + 1 = 2$

3. $-2 = \dfrac{y}{3}$

4. $\angle 1$ is a supplement of $\angle 2$, and $m\angle 2 = 87°$. Find $m\angle 1$.

5. A portable charger in the shape of a rectangular prism has a width of 3 inches. Its length is twice its height. The volume of the charger is 24 cubic inches. Find the length and height of the portable charger.

6. Consider the geometric sequence $-\dfrac{1}{3}, -1, -3, -9, \rightleftharpoons.$

   a. Describe the pattern.

   b. Write the next three terms of the sequence.

7. Rewrite the statements as a single biconditional statement.

   If your phone vibrates, then you have an unread notification.

   If you have an unread notification, then your phone vibrates.

2.3 Review & Refresh (continued)

In Exercises 8–10, use the diagram to determine whether you can assume the statement.

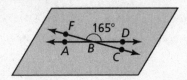

8. Points *A, B,* and *C* are coplanar.

9. $m\angle CBD = 15°$

10. $\overrightarrow{FB}$ bisects $\overline{AD}$.

2.3 Self-Assessment

Use the scale to rate your understanding of the learning target and the success criteria.

1 I do not understand yet.	**2** I can do it with help.	**3** I can do it on my own.	**4** I can teach someone else.

	Rating	Date
2.3 Postulates and Diagrams		
Learning Target: Interpret and sketch diagrams.	1 2 3 4	
I can identify postulates represented by diagrams.	1 2 3 4	
I can sketch a diagram given a verbal description.	1 2 3 4	
I can interpret a diagram.	1 2 3 4	

2.4 Review & Refresh

1. Name the definition, property, or postulate that is represented by the diagram.

$$JK + KL = JL$$

2. Solve $8x + 4y = 4$ for y. Justify each step.

3. Solve $4 > |x - 2|$. Graph the solution.

4. Rewrite the conditional statement in if-then form.

   A smartphone displays a warning when its battery drops below 10%.

5. You train athletes between 10 and 15 hours per week at a gym. You earn at least $10 per hour. Write a system that represents the situation.

6. Use inductive reasoning to make a conjecture about the square of an even number. Then use deductive reasoning to show that the conjecture is true.

2.4 Review & Refresh (continued)

7. Approximate when the function is positive, negative, increasing, or decreasing. Then describe the end behavior of the function.

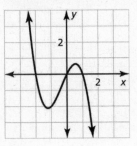

8. Write the property that justifies each step.

$2x + 17 = 45 - 2x$ Given

$4x + 17 = 45$ _____

$4x = 28$ _____

$x = 7$ _____

2.4 Self-Assessment

Use the scale to rate your understanding of the learning target and the success criteria.

| 1 | I do not understand yet. | 2 | I can do it with help. | 3 | I can do it on my own. | 4 | I can teach someone else. |

	Rating	Date
2.4 Algebraic Reasoning		
Learning Target: Use properties of equality to solve problems.	1 2 3 4	
I can identify algebraic properties of equality.	1 2 3 4	
I can use algebraic properties of equality to solve equations.	1 2 3 4	
I can use properties of equality to solve for geometric measures.	1 2 3 4	

2.5 Review & Refresh

1. Solve $9x^2 - 144 = 0$ using any method. Explain your choice of method.

2. Does the table represent a *linear* or *nonlinear* function?

x	1	3	4	5
y	2	4	6	8

3. $\angle 1$ is the complement of $\angle 3$, and $m\angle 3 = 7°$. Find $m\angle 1$.

4. Use inductive reasoning to make a conjecture about the sum of an integer and the square of the integer. Then use deductive reasoning to show that the conjecture is true.

5. Solve $-2(3x + 5) = 3x + 17$. Justify each step.

6. Name the property that $\angle D \cong \angle D$ illustrates.

2.5 Review & Refresh (continued)

7. A website host charges members an initial fee of $15 and a monthly fee of $3.75. Find the total cost of the first year of membership.

8. Sketch a diagram showing $\overrightarrow{BD}$ bisecting $\angle ABC$, so that $\angle ABD \cong \angle CBD$.

9. Complete the proof.

Given $PQ = RS$

Prove $PR = QS$

STATEMENTS	REASONS
1. $PQ = RS$	1. Given
2. $PQ + QR = RS + QR$	2. Addition Property
3. $PQ + QR = PR$	3. _____
4. $RS + QR = QS$	4. _____
5. $PR = QS$	5. Substitution Property of Equality

2.5 Self-Assessment

Use the scale to rate your understanding of the learning target and the success criteria.

| 1 | I do not understand yet. | 2 | I can do it with help. | 3 | I can do it on my own. | 4 | I can teach someone else. |

	Rating	Date
2.5 Proving Statements about Segments and Angles		
Learning Target: Prove statements about segments and angles.	1 2 3 4	
I can explain the structure of a two-column proof.	1 2 3 4	
I can write a two-column proof.	1 2 3 4	
I can identify properties of congruence.	1 2 3 4	

2.6 Review & Refresh

In Exercises 1 and 2, use the rectangular prism.

1. Name three collinear points.

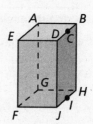

2. Write an example of the Three Point Postulate.

3. The final velocity v_f of an object is given by the formula $v_f = v_i + at$, where v_i is the initial velocity, a is the acceleration, and t is the time.

   a. Solve the formula for a.

   b. A vehicle with an initial velocity of 10 meters per second accelerates at a constant rate for four seconds. The final velocity of the vehicle is 15 meters per second. What is the acceleration?

4. Complete the square for $x^2 - 12x$. Then factor the trinomial.

5. Use the diagram and the given angle measure to find the other three measures.

   $m\angle 3 = 68°$

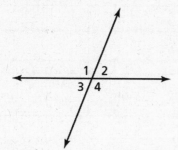

2.6   Review & Refresh (continued)

6. Complete the two-column proof.

Given $\angle ABD$ is a straight angle.

$\angle CBE$ is a straight angle.

Prove $\angle ABC \cong \angle DBE$

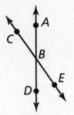

STATEMENTS	REASONS
1. $\angle ABD$ is a straight angle. $\angle CBE$ is a straight angle.	1. Given
2. $\angle ABC$ and $\angle CBD$ are supplementary.	2. _____ _____ _____
3. _____ _____ _____	3. Definition of supplementary angles
4. _____ _____ _____	4. Congruent Supplements Theorem

2.6   Self-Assessment

Use the scale to rate your understanding of the learning target and the success criteria.

| 1 | I do not understand yet. | 2 | I can do it with help. | 3 | I can do it on my own. | 4 | I can teach someone else. |

	Rating	Date
2.6 Proving Geometric Relationships		
Learning Target: Prove geometric relationships.	1 2 3 4	
I can prove geometric relationships by writing flowchart proofs.	1 2 3 4	
I can prove geometric relationships by writing paragraph proofs.	1 2 3 4	

Chapter Self-Assessment

Use the scale to rate your understanding of the learning target and the success criteria.

1 I do not understand yet. **2** I can do it with help. **3** I can do it on my own. **4** I can teach someone else.

	Rating	Date
Chapter 2 Reasoning and Proofs		
Learning Target: Understand reasoning and proofs.	1 2 3 4	
I can use inductive and deductive reasoning.	1 2 3 4	
I can justify steps using algebraic reasoning.	1 2 3 4	
I can explain postulates using diagrams.	1 2 3 4	
I can prove geometric relationships.	1 2 3 4	
2.1 Conditional Statements		
Learning Target: Understand and write conditional statements.	1 2 3 4	
I can identify the hypothesis and conclusion of a statement.	1 2 3 4	
I can write conditional statements and their related conditional statements.	1 2 3 4	
I can write biconditional statements.	1 2 3 4	
2.2 Inductive and Deductive Reasoning		
Learning Target: Use inductive and deductive reasoning.	1 2 3 4	
I can use inductive reasoning to make conjectures.	1 2 3 4	
I can use deductive reasoning to verify conjectures.	1 2 3 4	
I can distinguish between inductive and deductive reasoning.	1 2 3 4	
2.3 Postulates and Diagrams		
Learning Target: Interpret and sketch diagrams.	1 2 3 4	
I can identify postulates represented by diagrams.	1 2 3 4	
I can sketch a diagram given a verbal description.	1 2 3 4	
I can interpret a diagram.	1 2 3 4	

Chapter 2 — Chapter Self-Assessment (continued)

	Rating	Date
2.4 Algebraic Reasoning		
Learning Target: Use properties of equality to solve problems.	1 2 3 4	
I can identify algebraic properties of equality.	1 2 3 4	
I can use algebraic properties of equality to solve equations.	1 2 3 4	
I can use properties of equality to solve for geometric measures.	1 2 3 4	
2.5 Proving Statements about Segments and Angles		
Learning Target: Prove statements about segments and angles.	1 2 3 4	
I can explain the structure of a two-column proof.	1 2 3 4	
I can write a two-column proof.	1 2 3 4	
I can identify properties of congruence.	1 2 3 4	
2.6 Proving Geometric Relationships		
Learning Target: Prove geometric relationships.	1 2 3 4	
I can prove geometric relationships by writing flowchart proofs.	1 2 3 4	
I can prove geometric relationships by writing paragraph proofs.	1 2 3 4	

Chapter 2 — B.E.S.T. Test Prep

1. Which postulate is represented by the diagram?

  Ⓐ Three Point Postulate

  Ⓑ Line-Point Postulate

  Ⓒ Plane Intersection Postulate

  Ⓓ Line Intersection Postulate

2. What is the distance from $J(-2, 1)$ to $K(2, 1)$ in the coordinate plane?

  Ⓐ -4

  Ⓑ 0

  Ⓒ 2

  Ⓓ 4

3. Find the sum of the next three terms of the arithmetic sequence 8, 13, 18, 23, ...

4. $\angle 3$ and $\angle 4$ are vertical angles, and $m\angle 4 = 11.5°$. What is $m\angle 3$ in degrees?

5. Which statement has the same truth value as $q \rightarrow -p$

  Ⓐ $-p \rightarrow -q$

  Ⓑ $p \rightarrow -q$

  Ⓒ $-q \rightarrow -p$

  Ⓓ $q \rightarrow -p$

6. What is the value of x?

  Ⓐ -4

  Ⓑ -2

  Ⓒ 2

  Ⓓ 4

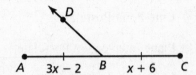

7. Select all the polynomials that are factored *completely*.

  Ⓐ $4x^2 + 2x = 2(2x^2 + x)$

  Ⓑ $x^4 - y^4 = (x^2 + y^2)(x^2 - y^2)$

  Ⓒ $3x + 6 = 3(x + 2)$

  Ⓓ $z^3 + 3z^2 + 6z + 9 = z^2(z + 3) + 6(z + 3)$

  Ⓔ $2w^4 + 4w^3 + w + 2 = (2w^3 + 1)(w + 2)$

8. What property is demonstrated below?

If $m\angle 1 = m\angle 2$, then $m\angle 1 + m\angle 3 = m\angle 2 + m\angle 3$.

_____

9. What is the inverse of $f(x) = \sqrt{x - 4}$?

  Ⓐ $f^{-1}(x) = 2x + 4$

  Ⓑ $f^{-1}(x) = x^2 + 4, x \geq 0$

  Ⓒ $f^{-1}(x) = x^2 - 4, x \geq 2$

  Ⓓ $f^{-1}(x) = x^2 + 4$

Chapter 2

B.E.S.T. Test Prep (continued)

10. Which is a counterexample to the conjecture that the sum of three consecutive whole numbers is even?

(A) $-4 + (-3) + (-2) = -9$

(C) $3 + 5 + 7 = 15$

(B) $1 + 2 + 3 = 6$

(D) $10 + 11 + 12 = 33$

11. Which reason corresponds with the fourth statement in the proof, "$m\angle ABD + m\angle DBE = m\angle CBE + m\angle DBE$?"

(A) Substitution Property of Equality

(B) Distributive Property

(C) Transitive Property of Equality

(D) Reflexive Property of Equality

Given $m\angle ABE = m\angle CBD$
Prove $m\angle ABD = m\angle CBE$

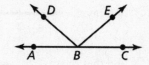

STATEMENTS	REASONS
1. $m\angle ABE = m\angle CBD$	1. Given
2. $m\angle ABE = m\angle ABD + m\angle DBE$	2. Angle Addition Postulate
3. $m\angle CBD = m\angle CBE + m\angle DBE$	3. Angle Addition Postulate
4. $m\angle ABD + m\angle DBE = m\angle CBE + m\angle DBE$	4.
5. $m\angle ABD + m\angle DBE - m\angle DBE = m\angle CBE + m\angle DBE - m\angle DBE$	5. Subtraction Property of Equality
6. $m\angle ABD = m\angle CBE$	6. Simplify.

12. Select all true equations.

(A) $5^0 \overset{?}{=} 0$

(B) $5^{-3} \cdot 5^8 \overset{?}{=} 5^5$

(C) $\dfrac{5^3}{5^5} \overset{?}{=} 5^2$

(D) $\left(5^2\right)^3 \overset{?}{=} 5^6$

(E) $\dfrac{5^{-4}}{5^3} \overset{?}{=} \dfrac{1}{5^7}$

13. Which point is the remaining vertex of a triangle with $A(-2, 1)$ and $B(-2, -5)$ that has an area of 6 square units?

(A) $C(0, 1)$

(B) $C(3, -2)$

(C) $C(-1, 1)$

(D) $C(4, 1)$

Chapter 2 **B.E.S.T. Test Prep** (continued)

14. Describe and graph the inequality $-1 \leq x \leq 2$.

Ⓐ four points;

Ⓑ line segment;

Ⓒ two rays;

Ⓓ line that passes through -1 and 2;

15. Rewrite the perimeter formula $P = r(\theta + 2)$ in terms of θ.

Ⓐ $\theta = P - r - 2$

Ⓑ $\theta = \dfrac{P}{r - 2}$

Ⓒ $\theta = \dfrac{P}{r} - 2$

Ⓓ $\theta = 2P - r$

16. Rewrite the conditional statement in if-then form. You cannot live chat when you log off.

Ⓐ If you log off, then you cannot live chat.

Ⓑ If you log off, then you can live chat.

Ⓒ If you cannot live chat, then you cannot log off.

Ⓓ If you can live chat, then you log off.

3.1 Review & Refresh

1. Copy the segment and construct a segment bisector by paper folding. Then label the midpoint M.

2. Solve the inequality $x + 8 < 13$. Graph the solution.

3. Name the property that the statement illustrates. If $\angle K \cong \angle L$, then $\angle L \cong \angle K$.

4. Classify the pair of numbered angles.

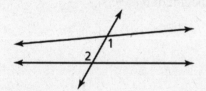

5. Solve the system.

$$y = \frac{1}{2}x + 3$$
$$y = \frac{1}{4}x + 1$$

6. Use the Transitive Property of Segment Congruence to complete the statement. If $\overline{WX} \cong \overline{YZ}$ and $\overline{YZ} \cong \overline{QR}$, then _____.

3.1 Review & Refresh (continued)

7. Write a proof using any format.

   Given M is the midpoint of $\overline{AB}$.

   $\overline{CM} \cong \overline{MB}$

   Prove $\overline{AM} \cong \overline{CM}$

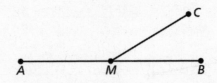

8. Write an equation of the line that passes through the point $(4, -2)$ and has a slope of -3.

9. Evaluate $\sqrt[3]{-27}$.

10. Find the volume of a cylinder with a radius of 7 meters and a height of 6 meters. Round your answer to the nearest tenth.

3.1 Self-Assessment

Use the scale to rate your understanding of the learning target and the success criteria.

| 1 | I do not understand yet. | 2 | I can do it with help. | 3 | I can do it on my own. | 4 | I can teach someone else. |

	Rating	Date
3.1 Pairs of Lines and Angles		
Learning Target: Understand lines, planes, and pairs of angles.	1 2 3 4	
I can identify lines and planes.	1 2 3 4	
I can identify parallel and perpendicular lines.	1 2 3 4	
I can identify pairs of angles formed by transversals.	1 2 3 4	

Name_____ Date_____

3.2 Review & Refresh

In Exercises 1–3, use the diagram.

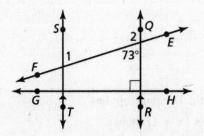

1. Name a pair of perpendicular lines.

2. Is $\overrightarrow{EF} \parallel \overrightarrow{GH}$? Explain.

3. Find $m\angle 1$ and $m\angle 2$. Tell which postulates or theorems you used.

In Exercises 4 and 5, name the property that the statement illustrates.

4. If $\overline{LM} \cong \overline{PR}$, then $\overline{PR} \cong \overline{LM}$.

5. If $\angle W \cong \angle X$ and $\angle X \cong \angle Y$, then $\angle W \cong \angle Y$.

In Exercises 6 and 7, factor the polynomial completely.

6. $16x^6 - 64x^4$

7. $y^3 - 7y^2 + 5y - 35$

3.2 Review & Refresh (continued)

8. Find the x- and y-intercepts of the graph of $3y - 8x = 24$.

9. A square painting is surrounded by a frame with uniform width. The painting has a side length of $(x - 2)$ inches. The side length of the frame is $(x + 1)$ inches.

   Write an expression for the area of the square frame. Then find the area of the frame when $x = 6$.

10. Find the value of x in the diagram.

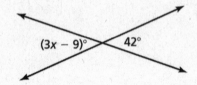

3.2 Self-Assessment

Use the scale to rate your understanding of the learning target and the success criteria.

| 1 | I do not understand yet. | 2 | I can do it with help. | 3 | I can do it on my own. | 4 | I can teach someone else. |

	Rating	Date
3.2 Parallel Lines and Transversals		
Learning Target: Prove and use theorems about parallel lines.	1 2 3 4	
I can use properties of parallel lines to find angle measures.	1 2 3 4	
I can prove theorems about parallel lines.	1 2 3 4	

Name_____ Date_____

In Exercises 1 and 2, find the distance between the two points.

1. $(8, 6)$ and $(0, -9)$

2. $(11, -2)$ and $(5, 3)$

3. Find the value of x.

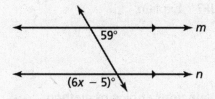

4. The height (in feet) of a ball t seconds after it is thrown can be represented by $h(t) = -16t^2 + 128t + 7$. Estimate and interpret the maximum value of the function.

5. Find the value of x that makes $k \parallel \ell$. Explain your reasoning.

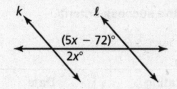

3.3 Review & Refresh (continued)

In Exercises 6 and 7, use the diagram.

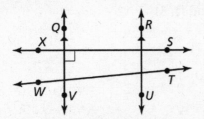

6. Name a pair of perpendicular lines.

7. Is $\overrightarrow{XS} \parallel \overrightarrow{WT}$? Explain.

In Exercises 8 and 9, solve the system using any method. Explain your choice of method.

8. $3x + 4y = 12$
$-6x - 5y = 30$

9. $y = 9x + 7$
$4x - y = -17$

10. Evaluate $f(x) = -8x + 14$ when $x = -3, 2,$ and 6.

3.3 Self-Assessment

Use the scale to rate your understanding of the learning target and the success criteria.

1 I do not understand yet.	**2** I can do it with help.	**3** I can do it on my own.	**4** I can teach someone else.

	Rating	Date
3.3 Proofs with Parallel Lines		
Learning Target: Prove and use theorems about identifying parallel lines.	1 2 3 4	
I can use theorems to identify parallel lines.	1 2 3 4	
I can construct parallel lines.	1 2 3 4	
I can prove theorems about identifying parallel lines.	1 2 3 4	

3.4 Review & Refresh

In Exercises 1 and 2, find the slope and the *y*-intercept of the graph of the linear equation.

1. $y = -\frac{2}{3}x + 1$

2. $7x + y = 16$

3. Two angles form a linear pair. The measure of one angle is 94°. Find the measure of the other angle.

4. Find the slope of the line that passes through $(-3, 8)$ and $(1, 6)$.

5. The post office and the bank are both on the same straight road between the school and your house. The distance from the school to the bank is 523 yards, the distance from the bank to your house is 803 yards, and the distance from the post office to your house is 391 yards.

   a. What is the distance from the post office to the bank?

   b. What is the distance from the school to your house?

6. Solve the system using any method.

   $y = x^2 + 3x - 1$
   $y = -2x - 5$

3.4 Review & Refresh (continued)

In Exercises 7–9, consider the lines that contain the segments in the figure and the planes that contain the faces of the figure. Which line(s) or plane(s) contain point M and appear to fit the description?

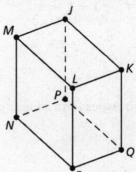

7. line(s) perpendicular to $\overleftrightarrow{JK}$

8. line(s) skew to $\overleftrightarrow{JK}$

9. plane(s) parallel to plane QRK

In Exercises 10 and 11, graph the function. Compare the graph to the graph of $f(x) = |x|$. Find the domain and range.

10. $g(x) = |x| - 7$

11. $h(x) = -\dfrac{3}{4}|x|$

3.4 Self-Assessment

Use the scale to rate your understanding of the learning target and the success criteria.

| 1 | I do not understand yet. | 2 | I can do it with help. | 3 | I can do it on my own. | 4 | I can teach someone else. |

	Rating	Date
3.4 Proofs with Perpendicular Lines		
Learning Target: Prove and use theorems about perpendicular lines.	1 2 3 4	
I can find the distance from a point to a line.	1 2 3 4	
I can construct perpendicular lines and perpendicular bisectors.	1 2 3 4	
I can prove theorems about perpendicular lines.	1 2 3 4	

3.5 Review & Refresh

1. Find the value of x that makes $m \parallel n$. Explain your reasoning.

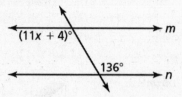

$(11x + 4)°$ m

$136°$ n

2. Make and test a conjecture about the product of three consecutive even numbers.

3. Find the perimeter of the triangle with the vertices $(2, 0)$, $(8, 5)$, and $(2, 7)$.

4. Solve the equation $\left(\dfrac{1}{3}\right)^x = 81$. Check your solution.

5. Determine which lines, if any, must be parallel. Explain your reasoning.

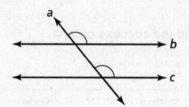

a b c

6. Factor $6x^2 + 7x + 2$.

7. Write an equation of the line passing through point $P(4, -3)$ that is parallel to $y = -2x + 9$.

3.5 Review & Refresh (continued)

8. Find the domain of $p(x) = \sqrt{8x + 3}$.

9. Solve $x^2 + 18x = 0$.

10. A chute forms a line between two parallel supports, as shown. Find $m\angle 2$. Explain your reasoning.

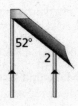

52°

2

11. Solve the inequality $4w + 11 \le 5w + 2w - 1$. Graph the solution.

12. Graph the quadratic function $y = (x - 3)(x + 1)$. Label the vertex, axis of symmetry, and x-intercepts. Find the domain and range of the function.

3.5 Self-Assessment

Use the scale to rate your understanding of the learning target and the success criteria.

1 I do not understand yet.	2 I can do it with help.	3 I can do it on my own.	4 I can teach someone else.

3.5 Equations of Parallel and Perpendicular Lines	Rating	Date
Learning Target: Partition a directed line segment and understand slopes of parallel and perpendicular lines.	1 2 3 4	
I can partition directed line segments using slope.	1 2 3 4	
I can use slopes to identify parallel and perpendicular lines.	1 2 3 4	
I can write equations of parallel and perpendicular lines.	1 2 3 4	
I can find the distance from a point to a line.	1 2 3 4	

Name_____ Date _____

Chapter Self-Assessment

Use the scale to rate your understanding of the learning target and the success criteria.

1 I do not understand yet. **2** I can do it with help. **3** I can do it on my own. **4** I can teach someone else.

	Rating	Date
Chapter 3 Parallel and Perpendicular Lines		
Learning Target: Understand and use parallel and perpendicular lines.	1 2 3 4	
I can describe angle relationships formed by parallel lines and a transversal.	1 2 3 4	
I can construct parallel and perpendicular lines.	1 2 3 4	
I can prove theorems involving parallel and perpendicular lines.	1 2 3 4	
I can write equations of parallel and perpendicular lines.	1 2 3 4	
3.1 Pairs of Lines and Angles		
Learning Target: Understand lines, planes, and pairs of angles.	1 2 3 4	
I can identify lines and planes.	1 2 3 4	
I can identify parallel and perpendicular lines.	1 2 3 4	
I can identify pairs of angles formed by transversals.	1 2 3 4	
3.2 Parallel Lines and Transversals		
Learning Target: Prove and use theorems about parallel lines.	1 2 3 4	
I can use properties of parallel lines to find angle measures.	1 2 3 4	
I can prove theorems about parallel lines.	1 2 3 4	
3.3 Proofs with Parallel Lines		
Learning Target: Prove and use theorems about identifying parallel lines.	1 2 3 4	
I can use theorems to identify parallel lines.	1 2 3 4	
I can construct parallel lines.	1 2 3 4	
I can prove theorems about identifying parallel lines.	1 2 3 4	

Chapter 3 — Chapter Self-Assessment (continued)

	Rating	Date
3.4 Proofs with Perpendicular Lines		
Learning Target: Prove and use theorems about perpendicular lines.	1 2 3 4	
I can find the distance from a point to a line.	1 2 3 4	
I can construct perpendicular lines and perpendicular bisectors.	1 2 3 4	
I can prove theorems about perpendicular lines.	1 2 3 4	
3.5 Equations of Parallel and Perpendicular Lines		
Learning Target: Partition a directed line segment and understand slopes of parallel and perpendicular lines.	1 2 3 4	
I can partition directed line segments using slope.	1 2 3 4	
I can use slopes to identify parallel and perpendicular lines.	1 2 3 4	
I can write equations of parallel and perpendicular lines.	1 2 3 4	
I can find the distance from a point to a line.	1 2 3 4	

Chapter 3 **B.E.S.T. Test Prep**

1. Which of the following statements *cannot* be assumed from the diagram?

   Ⓐ Points B, C, and F are collinear.

   Ⓑ $\overrightarrow{CF} \perp$ plane S

   Ⓒ $\overrightarrow{DE} \perp$ plane R

   Ⓓ $\overrightarrow{FB}$ intersects $\overleftrightarrow{CD}$ at point C.

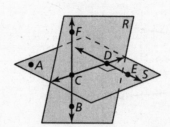

2. Identify the contrapositive of the given statement.
   Given Statement
   If two angles form a linear pair, then the angles are supplementary.

   Ⓐ If two angles do not form a linear pair, then the angles are not supplementary.

   Ⓑ If two angles are supplementary, then the angles form a linear pair.

   Ⓒ Two angles form a linear pair if and only if the angles are supplementary.

   Ⓓ If two angles are not supplementary, then the angles do not form a linear pair.

3. What is the value of x?

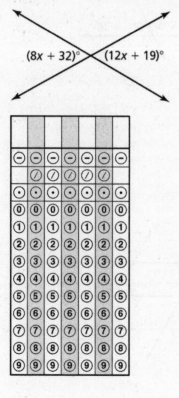

$(8x + 32)°$ $(12x + 19)°$

4. What is the value of x?

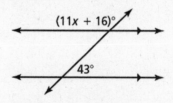

$(11x + 16)°$

$43°$

Chapter 3

B.E.S.T. Test Prep (continued)

5. Classify the pair of numbered angles.

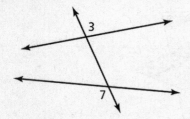

- Ⓐ alternate interior angles
- Ⓑ alternate exterior angles
- Ⓒ corresponding angles
- Ⓓ consecutive interior angles

6. What is the value of x that makes $m \parallel n$?

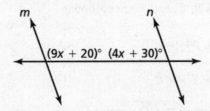

- Ⓐ 2
- Ⓑ 3
- Ⓒ 10
- Ⓓ 38

7. Point M is the midpoint of $\overline{AB}$. Find AB.

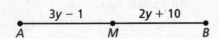

- Ⓐ 11
- Ⓑ 16
- Ⓒ 32
- Ⓓ 64

8. What is the value of y that makes $t \parallel u$?

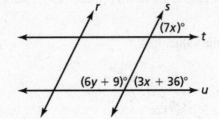

- Ⓐ 9
- Ⓑ 18
- Ⓒ 63
- Ⓓ 117

9. Select all the pairs of lines that must be parallel.

- Ⓐ $a \parallel c$
- Ⓑ $b \parallel c$
- Ⓒ $d \parallel e$
- Ⓓ $a \parallel b$

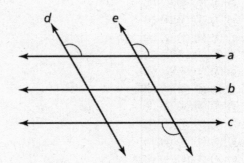

Chapter 3

B.E.S.T. Test Prep (continued)

10. Use the Law of Syllogism to write a new conditional statement that follows from the pair of true statements.

    If a figure is a square, then the figure has exactly four congruent sides. If a figure has exactly four congruent sides, then the figure is a rhombus.

    Ⓐ If a figure is a rhombus, then the figure is a square.

    Ⓑ A figure is a square if and only if the figure is a rhombus.

    Ⓒ If a figure is a square, then the figure is a rhombus.

    Ⓓ If a figure is not a square, then the figure is not a rhombus.

11. $\angle XYZ$ and $\angle LMN$ are complementary angles. $m\angle XYZ = (3x + 14)°$ and $m\angle LMN = (5x + 24)°$. What is $m\angle LMN$ in degrees?

12. Find the coordinates of point P along the directed line segment AB so that the ratio of AP to PB is 1 to 3.

    _____

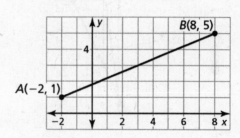

13. Which of the following is the remaining vertex of a triangle that has an area of 8 square units?

    Ⓐ $R(0, 3)$

    Ⓑ $S(-4, 5)$

    Ⓒ $T(2, 3)$

    Ⓓ $U(-4, 2)$

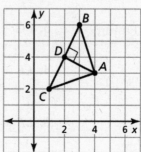

Chapter 3 B.E.S.T. Test Prep (continued)

14. Consider the lines that contain the segments in the figure and the planes that contain the faces of the figure. Select all the lines that appear parallel to $\overleftrightarrow{BC}$.

Ⓐ $\overleftrightarrow{AB}$

Ⓑ $\overleftrightarrow{AD}$

Ⓒ $\overleftrightarrow{EF}$

Ⓓ $\overleftrightarrow{HE}$

Ⓔ $\overleftrightarrow{DG}$

Ⓕ $\overleftrightarrow{HG}$

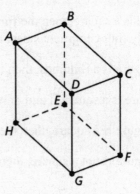

15. What is the distance from point A to $\overleftrightarrow{BC}$?

Ⓐ $5\sqrt{2}$

Ⓑ $\sqrt{5}$

Ⓒ $4\sqrt{2}$

Ⓓ 5

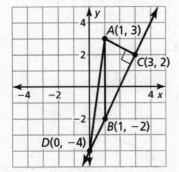

16. Which of the following statements is false?

Ⓐ Two planes intersect in a line.

Ⓑ Two points determine a line.

Ⓒ Two lines intersect in a point.

Ⓓ Any three points determine a plane.

17. Which reason corresponds with the fifth statement in the proof, "$EF = GH$?"

Ⓐ Subtraction Property of Equality

Ⓑ Segment Addition Postulate

Ⓒ Substitution Property of Equality

Ⓓ Reflexive Property of Equality

Given $EG = FH$

Prove $EF = GH$

STATEMENTS	REASONS
1. $EG = FH$	1. Given
2. $EF + FG = EG$	2. Segment Addition Postulate
3. $FG + GH = FH$	3. Segment Addition Postulate
4. $EF + FG = FG + GH$	4. Substitution Property of Equality
5. $EF = GH$	5. _____

4.1 Review & Refresh

1. Decide whether there is enough information to prove that $m \parallel n$. If so, state the theorem you can use.

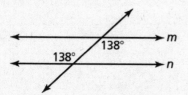

2. Write an equation of the line passing through point $P(-6, 4)$ that is perpendicular to $y + 8 = 2(x - 14)$. Graph the equations to check that the lines are perpendicular.

3. Graph quadrilateral $ABCD$ with vertices $A(-2, 4)$, $B(-1, 6)$, $C(4, 4)$, and $D(2, 3)$ and its image after the translation $(x, y) \rightarrow (x + 2, y - 3)$.

4. Write an equation for the nth term of the arithmetic sequence. Then find a_{10}.

   $7, 3, -1, -5, \ldots$

5. Solve the equation $50x = 2x^3$.

6. The function $h(x) = -16x^2 + 32x + 4$ models the height h (in feet) of a ball ejected from a ball launcher after x seconds. When is the ball at a height of 15 feet?

Name _____ Date _____

7. Graph the function $g(x) = -1.5x^2$. Compare the graph to the graph of $f(x) = x^2$.

8. Find the inverse of the function $f(x) = -\frac{3}{5}x + \frac{9}{5}$. Then graph the function and its inverse.

In Exercises 9 and 10, use the translation $(x, y) \rightarrow (x - 1, y + 5)$.

9. What is the image of $A(-4, 10)$?

10. What is the preimage of $B'(0, 0)$?

4.1 **Self-Assessment**

Use the scale to rate your understanding of the learning target and the success criteria.

| 1 | I do not understand yet. | 2 | I can do it with help. | 3 | I can do it on my own. | 4 | I can teach someone else. |

	Rating	Date
4.1 Translations		
Learning Target: Understand translations of figures.	1 2 3 4	
I can translate figures.	1 2 3 4	
I can write a translation rule for a given translation.	1 2 3 4	
I can explain what a rigid motion is.	1 2 3 4	
I can perform a composition of translations on a figure.	1 2 3 4	

Name_____ Date_____

4.2 Review & Refresh

1. Find the distance from point A to $\overleftrightarrow{XZ}$.

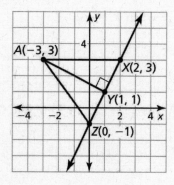

In Exercises 2 and 3, solve the equation by graphing.

2. $|3x| = |x - 4|$

3. $-2x + 8 = 3(x + 1)$

4. Graph $\triangle ABC$ with vertices $A(2, 3)$, $B(3, -1)$, and $C(-1, 2)$ and its image after a reflection in the x-axis.

5. Name the property that "If $\angle X \cong \angle Y$, then $\angle Y \cong \angle X$" illustrates.

6. Make a scatter plot of the data. Then describe the relationship between the data.

x	0.2	0.5	0.8	1.0	1.4	1.7	1.9	2.4
y	3.1	2.9	2.8	2.6	2.1	1.9	1.6	1.4

7. Find the distance from the point $(3, 7)$ to the line $y = \frac{1}{2}x + 3$.

4.2 Review & Refresh (continued)

8. Evaluate $h(x) = 4x - 9$ when $x = -2$.

9. Use the translation $(x, y) \rightarrow (x + 3, y - 2)$ to find the image of $A(-1, 6)$.

10. Factor $-4t^2 + 16t - 15$.

11. Find the product of $x - 8$ and $x + 10$.

12. Determine whether the figure has line symmetry. If so, draw the line(s) of symmetry and describe any reflections that map the figure onto itself.

4.2 Self-Assessment

Use the scale to rate your understanding of the learning target and the success criteria.

| 1 I do not understand yet. | 2 I can do it with help. | 3 I can do it on my own. | 4 I can teach someone else. |

	Rating	Date
4.2 Reflections		
Learning Target: Understand reflections of figures.	1 2 3 4	
I can reflect figures.	1 2 3 4	
I can perform compositions with reflections.	1 2 3 4	
I can identify line symmetry in polygons.	1 2 3 4	

4.3 Review & Refresh

1. $\overline{DF}$ bisects $\angle CDE$. If $m\angle CDF = 61°$, find $m\angle EDF$ and $m\angle CDE$.

2. The figures are congruent. Name the corresponding angles and the corresponding sides.

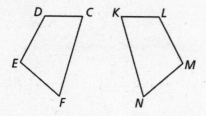

3. The endpoints of the directed line segment AB are $A(7, 4)$ and $B(2, 9)$. Find the coordinates of point P along segment AB so that the ratio of AP to PB is 3 to 2.

4. Graph the system. Identify a solution.

   $y > -x + 2$

   $y \le \frac{4}{5}x - 1$

5. Determine whether the table represents a *linear* or an *exponential* function. Explain.

x	−2	−1	0	1	2
f(x)	1	5	9	13	17

Name _____ Date _____

In Exercises 6 and 7, graph the polygon with the given vertices and its image after the indicated transformation.

6. $A(3, -2)$, $B(1, 5)$, $C(-2, 0)$

   Rotation: 180° about the origin

7. $W(0, 3)$, $X(-2, 1)$, $Y(-3, 3)$, $Z(-1, 5)$

   Rotation: 270° about the origin

8. Railways use railroad ties to secure the rails in place, as shown in the diagram. Each tie is parallel to the tie directly next to it. Explain why the leftmost tie is parallel to the rightmost tie.

4.3 Self-Assessment

Use the scale to rate your understanding of the learning target and the success criteria.

| 1 | I do not understand yet. | 2 | I can do it with help. | 3 | I can do it on my own. | 4 | I can teach someone else. |

	Rating	Date
4.3 Rotations		
Learning Target: Understand rotations of figures.	1 2 3 4	
I can rotate figures.	1 2 3 4	
I can perform compositions with rotations.	1 2 3 4	
I can identify rotational symmetry in polygons.	1 2 3 4	

4.4 Review & Refresh

In Exercises 1 and 2, solve the equation.

1. $-3(x - 4) = -7x$

2. $3n + 1 = \frac{1}{2}(8n - 4)$

3. Yesterday, you earned \$40 in tips. Today, you earned \$55 in tips. What is the percent of change?

4. Describe a congruence transformation that maps polygon $ABCD$ to polygon $QRST$.

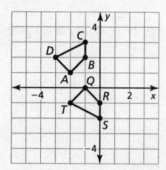

In Exercises 5 and 6, graph the linear equation. Identify the x-intercept.

5. $y = -2x + 7$

6. $4x - 2y = 16$

7. Write an inequality that represents the graph.

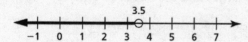

8. Let p be "you bake cookies" and let q be "you turn the oven on." Write the conditional statement $p \rightarrow q$, the converse $q \rightarrow p$, the inverse $-p \rightarrow -q$ and the contrapositive $-q \rightarrow -p$ in words. Then decide whether each statement is *true* or *false*

4.4   Review & Refresh (continued)

In Exercises 9 and 10, find the value of *x*. Show your steps.

9.

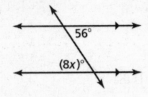

56°

(8x)°

10.

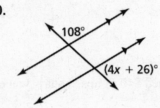

108°

(4x + 26)°

11. Graph these points and then determine whether the triangles with the given vertices are congruent. Use transformations to explain your reasoning.

Q(1, 3), R(4, 7), S(2, 6) and T(0, 5), U(3, 9), V(1, 8)

4.4   Self-Assessment

Use the scale to rate your understanding of the learning target and the success criteria.

| 1 | I do not understand yet. | 2 | I can do it with help. | 3 | I can do it on my own. | 4 | I can teach someone else. |

	Rating	Date
4.4 Congruence and Transformations		
Learning Target: Understand congruence transformations.	1 2 3 4	
I can identify congruent figures.	1 2 3 4	
I can describe congruence transformations.	1 2 3 4	
I can identify the types of symmetry in a tessellation.	1 2 3 4	
I can use congruence transformations to solve problems.	1 2 3 4	

4.5 Review & Refresh

In Exercises 1 and 2, graph the polygon with the given vertices and its image after the indicated transformation.

1. $D(-2, 1)$, $E(-3, 6)$, $F(1, 5)$, $G(2, 0)$

   Reflection: in the x-axis

2. $A(1, 3)$, $B(-1, 2)$, $C(2, 1)$

   Reflection: 180° about the origin

3. Simplify $\dfrac{9^{-1}x^{-5}}{3^{-3}x^{-2}y^0}$.

4. You are painting a rectangular canvas that is 21 inches wide and 27 inches long. Your friend is painting a rectangular canvas, where the width and length are each x inches shorter. When $x = 6$, what is the area of your friend's canvas?

5. Describe a congruence transformation that maps $\triangle ABC$ to $\triangle XYZ$.

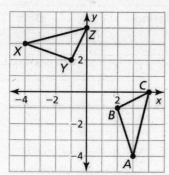

4.5 Review & Refresh (continued)

6. Graph $g(x) = 2(x + 3)^2 - 1$. Compare the graph to the graph of $f(x) = x^2$.

In Exercises 7 and 8, find the product.

7. $(4x - 7)^2$

8. $(y + 3)(8 - 5y)$

9. Solve the system using any method.

$2x + y = 3$
$x - 3y = 5$

10. Find the coordinates of the vertices of the image after a dilation with scale factor of $k = -\dfrac{1}{3}$.

$F(0, 4)$, $G(7, 12)$, $H(-3, 2)$

4.5 Self-Assessment

Use the scale to rate your understanding of the learning target and the success criteria.

| 1 | I do not understand yet. | 2 | I can do it with help. | 3 | I can do it on my own. | 4 | I can teach someone else. |

	Rating	Date
4.5 Dilations		
Learning Target: Understand dilations of figures.	1 2 3 4	
I can identify dilations.	1 2 3 4	
I can dilate figures.	1 2 3 4	
I can solve real-life problems involving scale factors and dilations.	1 2 3 4	

Name_____ Date_____

4.6 Review & Refresh

In Exercises 1–4, classify the angle.

1.

2.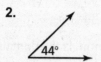
44°

3.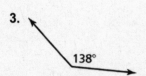
138°

4. ←————————→

5. Graph $\overline{PQ}$ with endpoints $P(-1, 4)$ and $Q(3, 1)$ and its image after the similarity transformation.

   Dilation: $(x, y) \rightarrow (2x, 2y)$

   Reflection: in the x-axis

6. Write an equation of the line passing through $(-2, 6)$ that is perpendicular to the line $y = -\frac{2}{3}x - 8$.

7. Solve $7x + 15 = 3x - 9$. Justify each step.

8. Determine whether the figure ABC and figure DEF with the given vertices are similar. Use transformations to explain your reasoning.

   $A(2, -1)$, $B(4, -1)$, and $C(4, 2)$
   $D(4, 2)$, $E(8, 2)$, and $F(8, -4)$

4.6   Review & Refresh (continued)

9. The linear function $j = 64 - 6g$ represents the amount of juice j (in fluid ounces) that you have left in a juice carton after pouring g glasses.

    a. Find the domain of the function. Is the domain discrete or continuous? Explain.

    b. Graph the function using its domain.

In Exercises 10 and 11, solve the inequality. Graph the solution.

10. $9 + 5x \le 3x - 1$ 11. $-3 < 2a + 3 < 15$

4.6   Self-Assessment

Use the scale to rate your understanding of the learning target and the success criteria.

1	I do not understand yet.	2	I can do it with help.	3	I can do it on my own.	4	I can teach someone else.

	Rating	Date
4.6 Similarity and Transformations		
Learning Target: Understand similarity transformations.	1 2 3 4	
I can perform similarity transformations.	1 2 3 4	
I can describe similarity transformations.	1 2 3 4	
I can prove that figures are similar.	1 2 3 4	

Name_____ Date_____

Chapter Self-Assessment

Use the scale to rate your understanding of the learning target and the success criteria.

	Rating	Date
Chapter 4 Transformations		
Learning Target: Understand transformations.	1 2 3 4	
I can identify transformations.	1 2 3 4	
I can perform translations, reflections, rotations, and dilations.	1 2 3 4	
I can describe congruence and similarity transformations.	1 2 3 4	
I can solve problems involving transformations.	1 2 3 4	
4.1 Translations		
Learning Target: Understand translations of figures.	1 2 3 4	
I can translate figures.	1 2 3 4	
I can write a translation rule for a given translation.	1 2 3 4	
I can explain what a rigid motion is.	1 2 3 4	
I can perform a composition of translations on a figure.	1 2 3 4	
4.2 Reflections		
Learning Target: Understand reflections of figures.	1 2 3 4	
I can reflect figures.	1 2 3 4	
I can perform compositions with reflections.	1 2 3 4	
I can identify line symmetry in polygons.	1 2 3 4	
4.3 Rotations		
Learning Target: Understand rotations of figures.	1 2 3 4	
I can rotate figures.	1 2 3 4	
I can perform compositions with rotations.	1 2 3 4	
I can identify rotational symmetry in polygons.	1 2 3 4	

Florida Geometry   **65**
B.E.S.T. Test Prep and Practice Workbook

Chapter Self-Assessment (continued)

	Rating	Date
4.4 Congruence and Transformations		
Learning Target: Understand congruence transformations.	1 2 3 4	
I can identify congruent figures.	1 2 3 4	
I can describe congruence transformations.	1 2 3 4	
I can identify the types of symmetry in a tessellation.	1 2 3 4	
I can use congruence transformations to solve problems.	1 2 3 4	
4.5 Dilations		
Learning Target: Understand dilations of figures.	1 2 3 4	
I can identify dilations.	1 2 3 4	
I can dilate figures.	1 2 3 4	
I can solve real-life problems involving scale factors and dilations.	1 2 3 4	
4.6 Similarity and Transformations		
Learning Target: Understand similarity transformations.	1 2 3 4	
I can perform similarity transformations.	1 2 3 4	
I can describe similarity transformations.	1 2 3 4	
I can prove that figures are similar.	1 2 3 4	

Chapter 4

B.E.S.T. Test Prep

1. Select all transformations that do not result in mapping $(a, -a)$ to (a, a) when $a > 0$.

   Ⓐ reflection in the y-axis

   Ⓑ reflection in the x-axis

   Ⓒ translation $2a$ units up

   Ⓓ translation a units up, followed by a reflection in the line $y = a$

   Ⓔ translation a units up, followed by a reflection in the line $y = \dfrac{a}{2}$

2. What is the next number in the sequence $-3, -2, 1, 6, 13, \ldots$?

_____

3. $\overrightarrow{BD}$ bisects $\angle ABC$. If $m\angle ABC = (6x + 58)°$, find $m\angle ABD$.

   Ⓐ $8°$

   Ⓑ $16°$

   Ⓒ $53°$

   Ⓓ $106°$

4. Use the dilation to find the value of y.

   Ⓐ 1.4

   Ⓑ 5

   Ⓒ 25

   Ⓓ 49

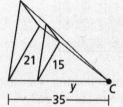

5. Which graph shows the image of $\triangle ABC$ after the glide reflection?

Translation: $(x, y) \rightarrow (x + 2, y + 3)$

Reflection: in the line $y = x$

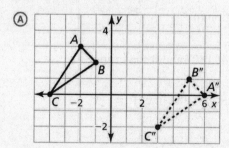

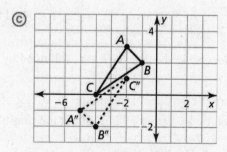

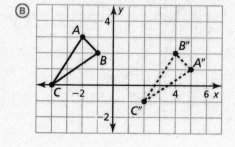

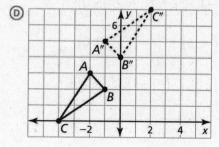

Chapter 4

B.E.S.T. Test Prep (continued)

6. What is the value of the expression $y - x$?

$(7x + 40)°$ $(17y + 73)°$

$(68 - 6y)°$ $(121 - 4x)°$

7. The vector $\langle 2, 6 \rangle$ describes the translation of $M(3, 2w)$ to $M'(4x - 2, 7)$ and $N(5y - 8, 9)$ to $N'\left(0, \dfrac{3}{2}z\right)$. What is the sum of $w, x, y,$ and z?

8. Which of the following is a congruence transformation that maps the preimage to the image?

Ⓐ reflection in the x-axis, followed by a rotation of 180° about the origin

Ⓑ reflection in the line $y = x$, followed by a reflection in the x-axis

Ⓒ rotation of 270° about the origin, followed by a reflection in the y-axis

Ⓓ reflection in the line $y = -x$, followed by a rotation of 180° about the origin

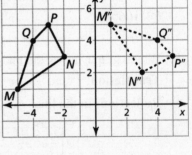

9. What are the vertices of the image of $\triangle XYZ$ after a reflection in the line $y = -x$, followed by a rotation of 270° about the origin?

Ⓐ $X''(-1, -5), Y''(1, 1), Z''(3, 0)$

Ⓑ $X''(-1, 5), Y''(1, -1), Z''(3, 0)$

Ⓒ $X''(1, 5), Y''(-1, -1), Z''(-3, 0)$

Ⓓ $X''(1, -5), Y''(-1, 1), Z''(-3, 0)$

Chapter 4

B.E.S.T. Test Prep (continued)

10. What is the area of the triangle?

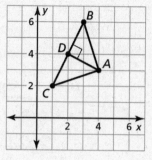

  Ⓐ $\dfrac{\sqrt{5}}{2}$ square units   Ⓒ 5 square units

  Ⓑ $\sqrt{5}$ square units   Ⓓ 10 square units

11. $AD = 29$. What is BC?

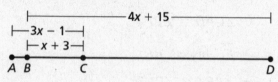

  Ⓐ 3   Ⓒ 8

  Ⓑ 6   Ⓓ 21

12. If the distance between m and n is 3.8 inches, what is the length of $\overline{RR''}$?

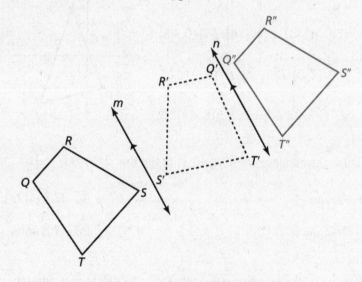

13. Write a rule for the translation of $\triangle ABC$ to $\triangle A'B'C'$.

_____

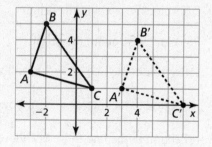

Chapter 4

B.E.S.T. Test Prep (continued)

14. What are the values of x that make $m \parallel n$?

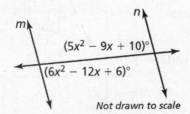

(5x² − 9x + 10)°
(6x² − 12x + 6)°

Not drawn to scale

  Ⓐ $x = -1$ and $x = 4$

  Ⓑ $x = -3$ and $x = 5$

  Ⓒ $x = 24$ and $x = 54$

  Ⓓ $x = 82$ and $x = 90$

15. Which of the following statements can you conclude from the diagram?

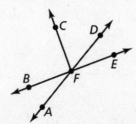

  Ⓐ $\angle CFD$ and $\angle DFE$ are complementary.

  Ⓑ $\angle CFD \cong \angle BFA$

  Ⓒ $\overrightarrow{FC}$ bisects $\overline{BE}$.

  Ⓓ $\angle BFA \cong \angle DFE$

16. What are the vertices of the image of $\triangle DEF$ after a dilation with scale factor 2, followed by a translation 2 units left and 4 units up?

  Ⓐ $D''(-3, 2), E''(-1, 7), F''(1, 1)$

  Ⓑ $D''(-6, -4), E''(2, 16), F''(10, -8)$

  Ⓒ $D''(-2, 0), E''(0, 5), F''(2, -1)$

  Ⓓ $D''(-8, 0), E''(0, 20), F(8, -4)$

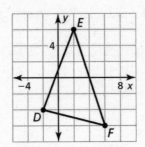

17. What is the distance from $A(-6, 1)$ to the line $3x - 4y = 16$?

  Ⓐ 0.5 unit   Ⓒ 27.1 units

  Ⓑ 7.6 units   Ⓓ 57.8 units

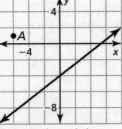

18. Select all of the transformations that are equivalent to a rotation of 90° about the origin.

  Ⓐ 270° clockwise about the origin

  Ⓑ 90° clockwise about the origin

  Ⓒ reflection in the line $y = -x$, followed by a reflection in the x-axis

  Ⓓ reflection in the line $y = x$, followed by a reflection in the y-axis

  Ⓔ reflection in the line $y = x$, followed by a reflection in the line $y = -x$

5.1 Review & Refresh

1. $\triangle DEF$ has vertices $D(-3, 5)$, $E(-1, 2)$, and $F(-4, 4)$. $\triangle GHI$ has vertices $G(-4, 1)$, $H(-2, -2)$, and $I(-5, 0)$. Determine whether $\triangle DEF$ is congruent to $\triangle GHI$. Use transformations to explain your reasoning.

2. Find the measure of each acute angle in a right triangle in which the measure of one acute angle is 4 times the measure of the other acute angle.

In Exercises 3 and 4, solve the equation.

3. $|11 - 4y| = 5$

4. $3t - 8 = -t$

5. Find the scale factor of the dilation. Then tell whether the dilation is a *reduction* or an *enlargement*.

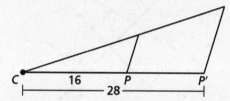

In Exercises 6 and 7, find the measure of the exterior angle.

6.

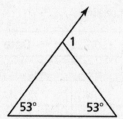

7.

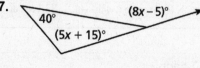

5.1 Review & Refresh (continued)

8. $\triangle ABC$ has vertices $A(6, 6)$, $B(9, 3)$, and $C(2, 2)$. Classify the triangle by its sides. Then determine whether it is a right triangle.

9. Describe a similarity transformation that maps $\triangle LMN$ to $\triangle XYZ$.

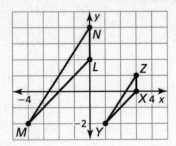

In Exercises 10 and 11, use the diagram.

10. Name a pair of parallel lines.

11. Name a pair of perpendicular lines.

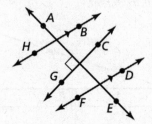

5.1 Self-Assessment

Use the scale to rate your understanding of the learning target and the success criteria.

1 I do not understand yet.	**2** I can do it with help.	**3** I can do it on my own.	**4** I can teach someone else.

	Rating	Date
5.1 Angles of Triangles		
Learning Target: Prove and use theorems about angles of triangles.	1 2 3 4	
I can classify triangles by sides and by angles.	1 2 3 4	
I can prove theorems about angles of triangles.	1 2 3 4	
I can find interior and exterior angle measures of triangles.	1 2 3 4	

5.2 Review & Refresh

1. Write a congruence statement for the triangles.
   Identify all pairs of congruent corresponding parts.

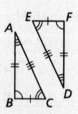

2. You design a logo for your chemistry club. The logo is 2 inches by 3 inches. You decide to dilate the logo to 5 inches by 7.5 inches. What is the scale factor of this dilation?

In Exercises 3 and 4, factor the polynomial.

3. $x^2 - 2x - 15$

4. $5x^2 + 17x - 12$

In Exercises 5 and 6, find the values of x and y.

5. $\triangle XYZ \cong \triangle RST$

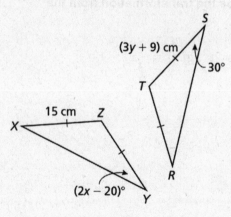

6. $ABCD \cong EFGH$

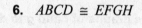
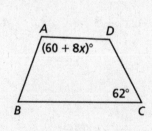
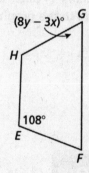

7. Show that the polygons are congruent. Explain your reasoning.

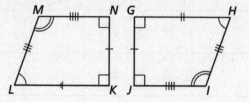

8. Find $m\angle 1$.

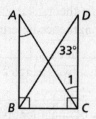

Name _____ Date _____

9. Find the measure of the exterior angle.

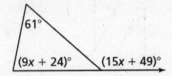

10. Graph $\triangle FGH$ with vertices $F(-4, 2)$, $G(2, 0)$, and $H(0, -4)$ and its image after the similarity transformation.

Rotation: 90° counterclockwise about the origin

Dilation: $(x, y) \rightarrow \left(\dfrac{3}{2}x, \dfrac{3}{2}y \right)$

In Exercises 11 and 12, use the graphs of *f* and *g* to describe the transformation from the graph of *f* to the graph of *g*.

11. $f(x) = |x|; g(x) = -|2x| + 3$

12. $f(x) = x^2; g(x) = \dfrac{1}{3}x^3 - 1$

5.2 **Self-Assessment**

Use the scale to rate your understanding of the learning target and the success criteria.

| 1 | I do not understand yet. | 2 | I can do it with help. | 3 | I can do it on my own. | 4 | I can teach someone else. |

	Rating	Date
5.2 Congruent Polygons		
Learning Target: Understand congruence in terms of rigid motions.	1 2 3 4	
I can use rigid motions to show that two triangles are congruent.	1 2 3 4	
I can identify corresponding parts of congruent polygons.	1 2 3 4	
I can use congruent polygons to solve problems.	1 2 3 4	

Name_____ Date_____

In Exercises 1 and 2, classify the triangle by its sides and by measuring its angles.

1.

2.

3. Graph $\triangle QRS$ with vertices $Q(-1, 2)$, $R(0, -1)$, and $S(-2, 1)$ and its image after the similarity transformation.

Rotation: 180° about the origin

Dilation: $(x, y) \rightarrow (3x, 3y)$

4. Decide whether enough information is given to prove that $\triangle PQR \cong \triangle STR$ by the SAS Congruence Theorem. Explain.

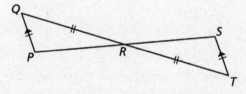

In Exercises 5 and 6, solve the inequality. Graph the solution.

5. $\dfrac{x}{2} + 8 \geq 5$

6. $|d - 3| < 9$

5.3 Review & Refresh (continued)

7. Find the values of x and y when $\triangle GHI \cong \triangle JKL$.

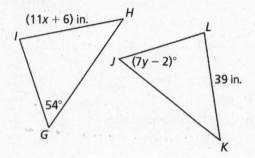

8. You want to determine the number of students in your school who own a cell phone. You survey 30 students at random. Twenty-four students own a cell phone, and six students do not. So, you conclude that 80% of the students in your school own a cell phone. Is your conclusion valid? Explain.

5.3 Self-Assessment

Use the scale to rate your understanding of the learning target and the success criteria.

1 I do not understand yet.	2 I can do it with help.	3 I can do it on my own.	4 I can teach someone else.

	Rating	Date
5.3 Proving Triangle Congruence by SAS		
Learning Target: Prove and use the Side-Angle-Side Congruence Theorem	1 2 3 4	
I can use rigid motions to prove the SAS Congruence Theorem.	1 2 3 4	
I can use the SAS Congruence Theorem.	1 2 3 4	

5.4 Review & Refresh

In Exercises 1 and 2, use the given property to complete the statement.

1. Symmetric Property of Angle Congruence:

    If $\angle E \cong \angle H$ then _____ $\cong$ _____.

2. Transitive Property of Angle Congruence:

    If $\angle W \cong \angle I$ and _____ $\cong$ _____, then $\angle W \cong \angle T$.

3. Find $m\angle 1$.

    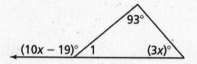

4. Graph $\overline{MN}$ with endpoints $M(2, 7)$ and $N(4, 1)$ and
    its image after the composition.

    Translation: $(x, y) \rightarrow (x + 2, y - 3)$

    Rotation: 90° about the origin

5. In the diagram, $ABCD \cong EFGH$. Find $m\angle F$ and GH.

    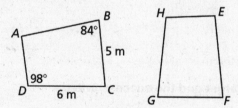

6. Find the distance from the point $(-6, -4)$ to the line $y = -3x + 8$.

7. Find the mean, median, mode, and range of the data set.

    26, 32, 16, 22, 30, 19, 23

Name _____ Date _____

In Exercises 8–10, find the values of *x* and *y*.

8.

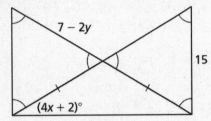

$7 - 2y$

15

$(4x + 2)°$

9.

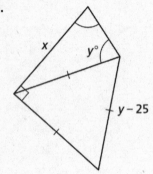

x

y°

y − 25

10.

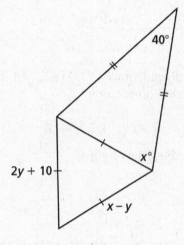

40°

x°

2*y* + 10

x − *y*

5.4   **Self-Assessment**

Use the scale to rate your understanding of the learning target and the success criteria.

| 1 | I do not understand yet. | 2 | I can do it with help. | 3 | I can do it on my own. | 4 | I can teach someone else. |

	Rating	Date
5.4 Equilateral and Isosceles Triangles		
Learning Target: Prove and use theorems about isosceles and equilateral triangles.	1 2 3 4	
I can prove and use theorems about isosceles triangles.	1 2 3 4	
I can prove and use theorems about equilateral triangles.	1 2 3 4	

5.5   Review & Refresh

1. Are $\overleftrightarrow{UW}$ and $\overleftrightarrow{XZ}$ parallel? Explain your reasoning.

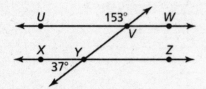

2. Find $m\angle 1$.

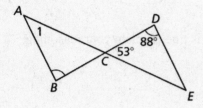

3. Write a linear function f with $f(1) = -1$ and $f(2) = 5$.

4. Find the values of x and y in the diagram of the roof shown.

5. Write a proof.

Given E is the midpoint of $\overline{AC}$ and $\overline{BD}$.
Prove $\triangle AEB \cong \triangle CED$

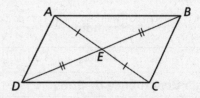

STATEMENTS	REASONS

5.5 Review & Refresh (continued)

6. Graph $y > 2x - 5$ in a coordinate plane.

7. Decide whether the congruence statement $\triangle DOG \cong \triangle CAT$ is true. Explain your reasoning.

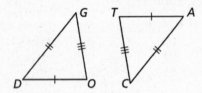

5.5 Self-Assessment

Use the scale to rate your understanding of the learning target and the success criteria.

| 1 | I do not understand yet. | 2 | I can do it with help. | 3 | I can do it on my own. | 4 | I can teach someone else. |

	Rating	Date
5.5 Proving Triangle Congruence by SSS		
Learning Target: Prove and use the Side-Side-Side Congruence Theorem.	1 2 3 4	
I can use rigid motions to prove the SSS Congruence Theorem.	1 2 3 4	
I can use the SSS Congruence Theorem.	1 2 3 4	
I can use the Hypotenuse-Leg Congruence Theorem.	1 2 3 4	

Name_____ Date_____

1. Find the coordinates of the midpoint of the line segment endpoints $C(-5, 2)$ and $D(3, -6)$.

2. You know that a pair of triangles has two pairs of congruent corresponding sides. What other information do you need to show that the triangles are congruent?

In Exercises 3 and 4, complete the statement. State which theorem you use.

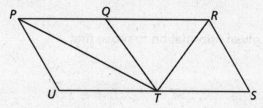

3. If $\angle QPT \cong \angle QTP$, then _____ $\cong$ _____.

4. If $\overline{QT} \cong \overline{QR}$, then $\angle$_____ $\cong \angle$_____.

5. You are using a microscope that shows the image of an object that is 10 times the object's actual size. Determine the length of the image of the bacteria seen through the microscope.

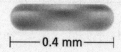

$\vdash$———0.4 mm———$\dashv$

5.6 Review & Refresh (continued)

In Exercises 6 and 7, decide whether enough information is given to prove that the triangles are congruent. If so, state the theorem you can use.

6. △XYW, △ZYW

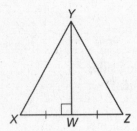

7. △ABC, △CDB

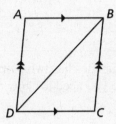

In Exercises 8 and 9, decide whether you can use the given information to prove that △LMN ≅ △PQR. Explain your reasoning.

8. ∠M ≅ ∠Q, ∠N ≅ ∠R, $\overline{NL}$ ≅ $\overline{RP}$

9. ∠L ≅ ∠R, ∠M ≅ ∠Q, $\overline{LM}$ ≅ $\overline{PQ}$

5.6 Self-Assessment

Use the scale to rate your understanding of the learning target and the success criteria.

| 1 | I do not understand yet. | 2 | I can do it with help. | 3 | I can do it on my own. | 4 | I can teach someone else. |

	Rating	Date
5.6 Proving Triangle Congruence by ASA and AAS		
Learning Target: Prove and use the Angle-Side-Angle Congruence Theorem and the Angle-Angle-Side Congruence Theorem.	1 2 3 4	
Use rigid motions to prove the ASA Congruence Theorem.	1 2 3 4	
I can prove the AAS Congruence Theorem.	1 2 3 4	
I can use the ASA and AAS Congruence Theorems.	1 2 3 4	

5.7 Review & Refresh

1. Explain how you can prove that $\angle B \cong \angle D$ using a paragraph proof.

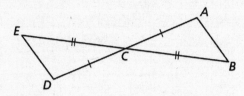

2. Find the perimeter of the polygon with vertices $J(-1, 1)$, $K(-3, 3)$, $L(-1, 5)$, and $M(1, 3)$.

In Exercises 3 and 4, decide whether enough information is given to prove that the triangles are congruent. If so, state the theorem you can use.

3. $\triangle PQR$, $\triangle STU$

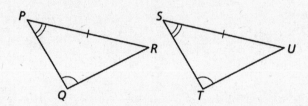

4. $\triangle WXY$, $\triangle YZW$

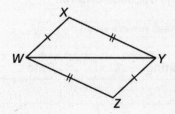

5.7 Review & Refresh (continued)

5. Find the value of x.

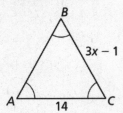

6. Simplify $(4m - 7) - (2 - 3m)$.

7. There are 2750 people in your town. The population of the town is increasing at an annual rate of 3.5%. Write and graph an exponential function to model the population of your town as a function of the number of years.

5.7 Self-Assessment

Use the scale to rate your understanding of the learning target and the success criteria.

1 I do not understand yet.	2 I can do it with help.	3 I can do it on my own.	4 I can teach someone else.

	Rating	Date
5.7 Using Congruent Triangles		
Learning Target: Use congruent triangles in proofs and to measure distances.	1 2 3 4	
I can use congruent triangles to prove statements.	1 2 3 4	
I can use congruent triangles to solve real-life problems.	1 2 3 4	
I can use congruent triangles to prove constructions.	1 2 3 4	

5.8 Review & Refresh

In Exercises 1 and 2, place the figure in a coordinate plane in a convenient way. Assign coordinates to each vertex. Explain the advantages of your placement.

1. an obtuse triangle with a height of 3 units and a base of 2 units

2. a rectangle with a length of $2w$

3. Graph the triangle with vertices $A(0, 0)$, $B(3m, m)$, and $C(0, 3m)$. Find the length and the slope of each side of the triangle. Find the coordinates of the midpoint of each side. Is the triangle a right triangle? isosceles? Explain. (Assume all variables are positive.)

4. Write a plan for the proof.

   Given Coordinates of vertices of $\triangle OPR$ and $\triangle QRP$

   Prove $\triangle OPR \cong \triangle QRP$

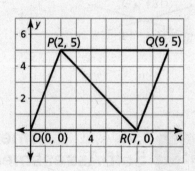

5. Write a coordinate proof.

   Given Coordinates of vertices of $\triangle OEF$ and $\triangle OGF$

   Prove $\triangle OEF \cong \triangle OGF$

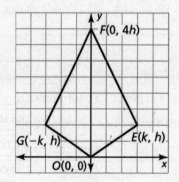

5.8 Review & Refresh (continued)

6. The coordinates of the vertices of a triangle are $A(0, 0)$, $B(11, 25)$, and $C(18, 0)$.
Prove that $\triangle ABC$ is a scalene triangle.

7. Place a rectangle with a length of $3w$ units in a coordinate plane in a convenient
way for finding the length of the diagonal. Assign coordinates to each vertex.

8. Find the value of x.

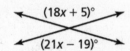

$(18x + 5)^\circ$

$(21x - 19)^\circ$

5.8 Self-Assessment

Use the scale to rate your understanding of the learning target and the success criteria.

1 I do not understand yet.	**2** I can do it with help.	**3** I can do it on my own.	**4** I can teach someone else.

	Rating	Date
5.8 Coordinate Proofs		
Learning Target: Use coordinates to write proofs.	1 2 3 4	
I can place figures in a coordinate plane.	1 2 3 4	
I can write plans for coordinate proofs.	1 2 3 4	
I can write coordinate proofs.	1 2 3 4	

Name_____ Date_____

Chapter Self-Assessment

Use the scale to rate your understanding of the learning target and the success criteria.

1 I do not understand yet.   **2** I can do it with help.   **3** I can do it on my own.   **4** I can teach someone else.

	Rating	Date
Chapter 5 Congruent Triangles		
Learning Target: Understand congruent triangles.	1 2 3 4	
I can classify triangles by sides and angles.	1 2 3 4	
I can solve problems involving congruent triangles.	1 2 3 4	
I can use different theorems to prove two triangles are congruent.	1 2 3 4	
I can write a coordinate proof.	1 2 3 4	
5.1 Angles of Triangles		
Learning Target: Prove and use theorems about angles of triangles.	1 2 3 4	
I can classify triangles by sides and by angles.	1 2 3 4	
I can prove theorems about angles of triangles.	1 2 3 4	
I can find interior and exterior angle measures of triangles.	1 2 3 4	
5.2 Congruent Polygons		
Learning Target: Understand congruence in terms of rigid motions.	1 2 3 4	
I can use rigid motions to show that two triangles are congruent.	1 2 3 4	
I can identify corresponding parts of congruent polygons.	1 2 3 4	
I can use congruent polygons to solve problems.	1 2 3 4	
5.3 Proving Triangle Congruence by SAS		
Learning Target: Prove and use the Side-Angle-Side Congruence Theorem.	1 2 3 4	
I can use rigid motions to prove the SAS Congruence Theorem.	1 2 3 4	
I can use the SAS Congruence Theorem.	1 2 3 4	

Chapter 5

Chapter Self-Assessment (continued)

	Rating	Date
5.4 Equilateral and Isosceles Triangles		
Learning Target: Prove and use theorems about isosceles and equilateral triangles.	1 2 3 4	
I can prove and use theorems about isosceles triangles.	1 2 3 4	
I can prove and use theorems about equilateral triangles.	1 2 3 4	
5.5 Proving Triangle Congruence by SSS		
Learning Target: Prove and use the Side-Side-Side Congruence Theorem.	1 2 3 4	
I can use rigid motions to prove the SSS Congruence Theorem.	1 2 3 4	
I can use the SSS Congruence Theorem.	1 2 3 4	
I can use the Hypotenuse-Leg Congruence Theorem.	1 2 3 4	
5.6 Proving Triangle Congruence by ASA and AAS		
Learning Target: Prove and use the Angle-Side-Angle Congruence Theorem and the Angle-Angle-Side Congruence Theorem.	1 2 3 4	
I can use rigid motions to prove the ASA Congruence Theorem.	1 2 3 4	
I can prove the AAS Congruence Theorem.	1 2 3 4	
I can use the ASA and AAS Congruence Theorems.	1 2 3 4	
5.7 Using Congruent Triangles		
Learning Target: Use congruent triangles in proofs and to measure distances.	1 2 3 4	
I can use congruent triangles to prove statements.	1 2 3 4	
I can use congruent triangles to solve real-life problems.	1 2 3 4	
I can use congruent triangles to prove constructions.	1 2 3 4	
5.8 Coordinate Proofs		
Learning Target: Use coordinates to write proofs.	1 2 3 4	
I can place figures in a coordinate plane.	1 2 3 4	
I can write plans for coordinate proofs.	1 2 3 4	
I can write coordinate proofs.	1 2 3 4	

Chapter 5 · B.E.S.T. Test Prep

1. Which of the following vertices form a right triangle?

Ⓐ $(3, -1), (4, 0), (6, -3)$

Ⓑ $(8, 8), (5, 1), (3, 5)$

Ⓒ $(0, 3), (7, 0), (1, 1)$

Ⓓ $(-5, 2), (-4, 7), (-2, 4)$

2. $ABCD \cong SRQT$. What is the value of x?

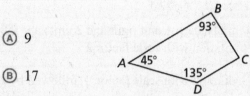

Ⓐ 9

Ⓑ 17

Ⓒ 24

Ⓓ 135

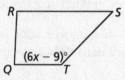

3. Find the area, in square units, of a triangle with vertices $X(4, 3.5)$, $Y(4, 5)$, and $Z(7.25, 5)$.

4. What is the distance, in units, from the point $(-3, 8)$ to the line $-4y = 8 - 3x$?

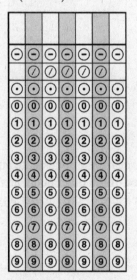

5. The vertex angle of isosceles $\triangle ABC$ is $\angle C$. What can you prove? Select all that apply.

Ⓐ $\overline{AB} \cong \overline{BC}$

Ⓑ $\angle A \cong \angle B$

Ⓒ $\angle B \cong \angle C$

Ⓓ $\overline{BC} \cong \overline{AC}$

Ⓔ $\overline{AB} \cong \overline{AC}$

6. $\overline{XY}$ has endpoints $X(-3, 1)$ and $Y(4, -5)$. What is the midpoint of its image after a 90° rotation about the origin?

_____

7. Which of the following similarity transformations map $\triangle ABC$ to $\triangle A''B''C''$? Select all that apply.

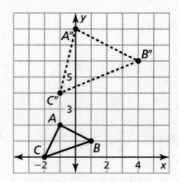

Ⓐ translation 1 unit right and 2 units up, followed by a dilation with scale factor 2

Ⓑ dilation with scale factor $\frac{1}{2}$, followed by a translation 1 unit left and 2 units down

Ⓒ dilation with scale factor 2, followed by a translation 2 units right and 4 units up

Ⓓ translation 2 units left and 4 units down, followed by a dilation with scale factor $\frac{1}{2}$

Ⓔ dilation with scale factor 2, followed by a translation 2 units left and 4 units down

8. What is the length of the diagonal of the figure?

_____

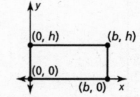

9. Two parallel lines are cut by a transversal. Which angle pairs are supplementary?

Ⓐ corresponding angles

Ⓑ alternate interior angles

Ⓒ alternate exterior angles

Ⓓ consecutive interior angles

10. In a right triangle, the measure of one acute angle is 2 times the difference of the other acute angle and 12. What is the measure of the smaller angle?

Ⓐ 38°

Ⓑ 52°

Ⓒ 57°

Ⓓ 34°

11. Which property of equality illustrates the statement "If $AC = 14$, then $BD + AC = BD + 14$?"

Ⓐ Transitive Property of Equality

Ⓑ Symmetric Property of Equality

Ⓒ Division Property of Equality

Ⓓ Substitution Property of Equality

12. What is the value of x?

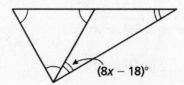

$(8x - 18)°$

Ⓐ 6

Ⓑ 9.75

Ⓒ 17.25

Ⓓ 30

Chapter 5

B.E.S.T. Test Prep (continued)

13. Which of the following are corresponding angles?

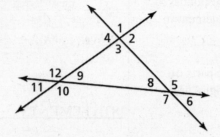

Ⓐ ∠1 and ∠8

Ⓑ ∠2 and ∠10

Ⓒ ∠4 and ∠8

Ⓓ ∠2 and ∠5

14. Which theorem can you use to prove that the triangles are congruent?

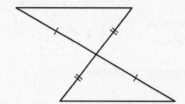

Ⓐ SSS Congruence Theorem

Ⓑ SAS Congruence Theorem

Ⓒ ASA Congruence Theorem

Ⓓ AAS Congruence Theorem

15. Find the value of *x*.

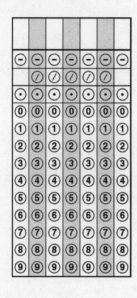

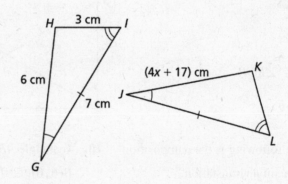

16. Two points lie in a plane. What can you conclude about the line containing the two points?

Ⓐ The line is parallel to the plane.

Ⓑ The line lies in the plane.

Ⓒ The line is perpendicular to the plane.

Ⓓ The line cannot exist.

B.E.S.T. Test Prep (continued)

17. Which reason corresponds with the second statement in the proof, "$\overline{XZ} \cong \overline{ZX}$?"

Ⓐ Corresponding parts of congruent triangles are congruent.

Ⓑ Reflexive Property of Segment Congruence

Ⓒ Symmetric Property of Segment Congruence

Ⓓ Definition of congruent segments

Given $\overline{WX} \cong \overline{YZ}$, $\overline{XY} \cong \overline{ZW}$

Prove $\triangle WXZ \cong \triangle YZX$

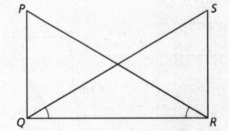

STATEMENTS	REASONS
1. $\overline{WX} \cong \overline{YZ}$, $\overline{XY} \cong \overline{ZW}$	1. Given
2. $\overline{XZ} \cong \overline{ZX}$	2.
3. $\triangle WXZ \cong \triangle YZX$	3. SSS Congruence Theorem

18. What additional information do you need to prove that $\triangle PQR \cong \triangle SRQ$ by the ASA Congruence Theorem?

Ⓐ $\angle P \cong \angle S$

Ⓑ $\overline{PQ} \cong \overline{SR}$

Ⓒ $\angle QRS \cong \angle RQP$

Ⓓ $\overline{SQ} \cong \overline{PR}$

19. Which of the following is the composition rewritten as a single translation?

Translation: $(x, y) \to (x + 9, y - 8)$

Translation: $(x, y) \to (x - 3, y - 4)$

Ⓐ $(x, y) \to (x + 6, y - 12)$

Ⓑ $(x, y) \to (x + 12, y - 4)$

Ⓒ $(x, y) \to (x + 6, y - 4)$

Ⓓ $(x, y) \to (x + 12, y - 12)$

20. Rectangle $ABCD$ has vertices $A(0, 12)$, $B(6, 0)$, $C(0, -3)$, and $D(-6, 9)$. What is the area of the image after a dilation with a scale factor of $\frac{2}{3}$?

Ⓐ 90 square units

Ⓑ 40 square units

Ⓒ 202.5 square units

Ⓓ 60 square units

21. Complete the congruence statement.

$\triangle DEF \cong$ _____

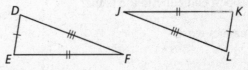

6.1 Review & Refresh

In Exercises 1 and 2, classify the triangle by its angles and sides.

1.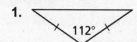
   112°

2.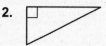

3. A stair railing is designed as shown. Find $m\angle 2$. Explain your reasoning.

   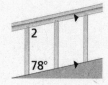
   2
   78°

4. Use the given information to prove that $\triangle DAC \cong \triangle BCA$.
   Given $\angle ADE \cong \angle CBE$,
   $\overline{DE} \cong \overline{BE}$
   Prove $\triangle DAC \cong \triangle BCA$

   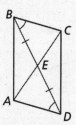

5. Find the product of $-3x^4$ and $2x^3 - 8x + 13$.

6. In $\triangle STU$ and $\triangle WXY$, $\overline{TU} \cong \overline{XY}$ and $\overline{SU} \cong \overline{WY}$. What is the third congruence statement that is needed to prove that $\triangle STU \cong \triangle WXY$ using the SSS Congruence Theorem? the SAS Congruence Theorem?

6.1 Review & Refresh (continued)

In Exercises 7 and 8, find the indicated measure. Explain your reasoning.

7. *EG*

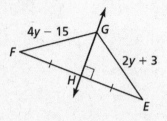

8. *m∠LMN*

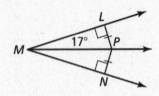

6.1 Self-Assessment

Use the scale to rate your understanding of the learning target and the success criteria.

| 1 | I do not understand yet. | 2 | I can do it with help. | 3 | I can do it on my own. | 4 | I can teach someone else. |

	Rating	Date
6.1 Perpendicular and Angle Bisectors		
Learning Target: Use theorems about perpendicular and angle bisectors.	1 2 3 4	
I can identify a perpendicular bisector and an angle bisector.	1 2 3 4	
I can use theorems about bisectors to find measures in figures.	1 2 3 4	
I can write equations of perpendicular bisectors.	1 2 3 4	

6.2 Review & Refresh

1. Determine whether $\triangle QRS$ and $\triangle TUV$ with the given vertices are congruent. Use transformations to explain your reasoning.

   $Q(-4, 5),\ R(2, 7),\ S(0, 2)$

   $T(-1, 3),\ U(5, 5),\ V(3, 0)$

2. Find $m\angle 1$. Then classify the triangle by its angles.

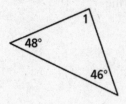

3. Explain how to prove that $\angle CDF \cong \angle EDF$.

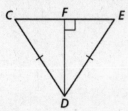

4. Factor $4h^6 - 64h^4$.

5. Find CD.

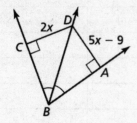

6.2 Review & Refresh (continued)

6. A triangle has vertices $X(-5, 1)$, $Y(5, 3)$, and $Z(3, -7)$. Prove that $\triangle XYZ$ is isosceles.

7. The endpoints of $\overline{JK}$ are $J(-3, 6)$ and $K(-3, 0)$. Find the coordinates of the midpoint M. Then find JK.

8. Determine whether the table represents a *linear* or *nonlinear* function. Explain.

x	1	4	7	10
y	2	-2	-6	-10

6.2 Self-Assessment

Use the scale to rate your understanding of the learning target and the success criteria.

1 I do not understand yet.	**2** I can do it with help.	**3** I can do it on my own.	**4** I can teach someone else.

	Rating	Date
6.2 Bisectors of Triangles		
Learning Target: Use bisectors of triangles.	1 2 3 4	
I can find the circumcenter and incenter of a triangle.	1 2 3 4	
I can circumscribe a circle about a triangle.	1 2 3 4	
I can inscribe a circle within a triangle.	1 2 3 4	
I can use points of concurrency to solve real-life problems.	1 2 3 4	

Name_____ Date_____

6.3 Review & Refresh

1. Find $m\angle BDC$. Explain your reasoning.

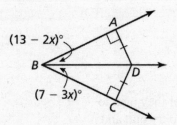

2. Find the coordinates of the circumcenter of the triangle with vertices
$A(-2, 5)$, $B(4, 2)$, and $C(-2, -2)$.

3. Tell whether the orthocenter of $\triangle XYZ$ with vertices $X(-4, 2)$, $Y(6, 7)$, and
$Z(-6, 16)$ is *inside*, *on*, or *outside* the triangle. Then find its coordinates.

4. $\overline{AB}$ has endpoints $A(5, 7)$ and $B(-1, 3)$. $\overline{CD}$ has endpoints $C(2, 1)$ and $D(4, -2)$.
Is $\overline{AB} \parallel \overline{CD}$?

In Exercises 5 and 6, solve the system.

5. $7x = 11 - 2y$
$2x + y = 1$

6. $4y - 3x = -7$
$x - y = 2$

7. Find the coordinates of the centroid of the triangle with vertices $A(-2, 5)$, $B(4, 2)$, and
$C(-2, -2)$.

6.3 Review & Refresh (continued)

In Exercises 8 and 9, solve the equation.

8. $2n^2 + 50 = 0$

9. $x^2 - 15 = -4x$

10. You conduct a survey that asks 188 students in your school whether they plan to try out for the cross country team. Forty-nine of the students plan to try out, and 21 of those students are males. Sixty-seven of the females surveyed do not plan to try out. Organize the results in a two-way table. Include the marginal frequencies.

11. Write a plan for proof.

   Given $\overline{WY} \perp \overline{XZ}$

   Prove $\triangle WXY \cong \triangle WZY$

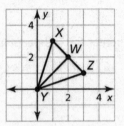

6.3 Self-Assessment

Use the scale to rate your understanding of the learning target and the success criteria.

| 1 | I do not understand yet. | 2 | I can do it with help. | 3 | I can do it on my own. | 4 | I can teach someone else. |

	Rating	Date
6.3 Medians and Altitudes of Triangles		
Learning Target: Use medians and altitudes of triangles.	1 2 3 4	
I can draw medians and altitudes of triangles.	1 2 3 4	
I can find the centroid of a triangle.	1 2 3 4	
I can find the orthocenter of a triangle.	1 2 3 4	

6.4 Review & Refresh

1. Find a counterexample to show that the conjecture is false.

   Conjecture The sum of two numbers is always positive.

2. Find *JK*. Explain your reasoning.

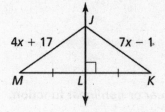

3. Find the coordinates of the centroid of $\triangle RST$ with vertices $R(3, 1)$, $S(7, 3)$, and $T(5, 5)$.

4. The incenter of $\triangle ABC$ is point *N*. $NQ = 4x + 3$ and $NS = 5x + 1$. Find *NR*.

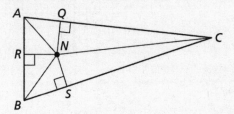

5. $\overline{MN}$ is a midsegment of $\triangle XYZ$. Find the values of *x* and *y*.

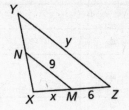

6.4 Review & Refresh (continued)

6. Write a piecewise function that represents the total cost y (in dollars) of renting a bicycle for x hours. Then determine the total cost for 435 minutes.

Bicycle Rentals

Time	Price
up to 3 hours	$15
up to 6 hours	$25
up to 9 hours	$35
up to 12 hours	$45
$25 rental fee required	

In Exercises 7 and 8, determine whether the equation represents a *linear* or *nonlinear* function. Explain.

7. $y = -1$

8. $y = 2x^2 - 3$

9. Use the graph of $\triangle ABC$ with midsegments $\overline{DE}$, $\overline{EF}$, and $\overline{DF}$ to find the coordinates of D, E, and F.

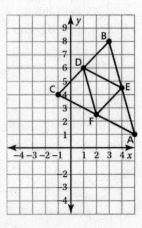

6.4 Self-Assessment

Use the scale to rate your understanding of the learning target and the success criteria.

| 1 | I do not understand yet. | 2 | I can do it with help. | 3 | I can do it on my own. | 4 | I can teach someone else. |

	Rating	Date
6.4 The Triangle Midsegment Theorem		
Learning Target: Find and use midsegments of triangles.	1 2 3 4	
I can use midsegments of triangles in the coordinate plane to solve problems.	1 2 3 4	
I can solve real-life problems involving midsegments.	1 2 3 4	

6.5   Review & Refresh

1. $\triangle DEF$ has vertices $D(2, 7)$, $E(-4, 1)$, and $F(4, 3)$. Find the coordinates of the vertices of the midsegment triangle of $\triangle DEF$.

2. You have an old photograph that is 8 inches by 6 inches. You enlarge the photograph to 12 inches by 9 inches to hang on your wall. What is the scale factor of this dilation?

3. The incenter of $\triangle XYZ$ is point N. $NQ = 2x - 4$ and $NS = -3x + 11$. Find NR.

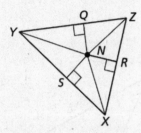

4. Tell whether the orthocenter of $\triangle QRS$ with vertices $Q(5, 12)$, $R(2, 3)$, and $S(6, 7)$ is *inside*, *on*, or *outside* the triangle. Then find its coordinates.

5. Graph $\overline{XY}$ with endpoints $X(3, -5)$ and $Y(-2, 1)$ and its image after a reflection in the y-axis, followed by a rotation of $90°$ about the origin.

6. Decide whether enough information is given to prove that $\triangle ABE \cong \triangle DCE$. If so, state the theorem you would use.

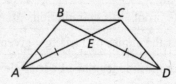

Name _____ Date _____

7. Find the value of x.

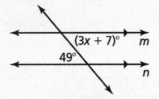

(3x + 7)°   m
49° n

8. Solve $\frac{2}{5}x - \frac{4}{3}y = 2$ for y. Justify each step.

9. List the angles of the triangle in order from smallest to largest.

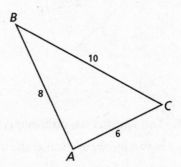

Use the scale to rate your understanding of the learning target and the success criteria.

1	I do not understand yet.	**2**	I can do it with help.	**3**	I can do it on my own.	**4**	I can teach someone else.

	Rating	Date
6.5 Proof by Contradiction and Inequalities in One Triangle		
Learning Target: Write proofs by contradiction and understand inequalities in a triangle.	1 2 3 4	
I can write proofs by contradiction. **H**	1 2 3 4	
I can order the angles of a triangle given the side lengths.	1 2 3 4	
I can order the side lengths of a triangle given the angle measures.	1 2 3 4	
I can determine possible side lengths of triangles.	1 2 3 4	

6.6 Review & Refresh

In Exercises 1 and 2, find the value of x.

1.
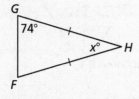

2. $\overline{DE}$ is a midsegment of $\triangle ABC$.

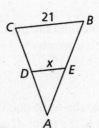

3. Graph quadrilateral $WXYZ$ with vertices $W(2, 1)$, $X(5, -2)$, $Y(2, -5)$, and $Z(-1, -2)$ and its image after the similarity transformation.

   Translation: $(x, y) \rightarrow (x + 1, y + 2)$

   Dilation: $(x, y) \rightarrow \left(\frac{1}{3}x, \frac{1}{3}y\right)$

4. Which is longer, $\overline{AB}$ or $\overline{QR}$? Explain your reasoning.

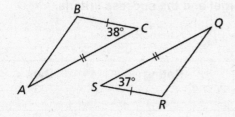

6.6 Review & Refresh (continued)

5. A city planner wants to build a gazebo. The planner sketches one possible location of the gazebo represented by point *P*.

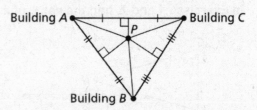

a. Which point of concurrency did the planner use in the sketch as the location of the gazebo?

b. The planner wants the gazebo to be equidistant from the sidewalks connecting the three buildings. Should the point of concurrency in the sketch be the location of the gazebo? If not, which point of concurrency should the planner use? Explain.

6. What possible angle measures exist for $\angle JKL$? Explain your reasoning.

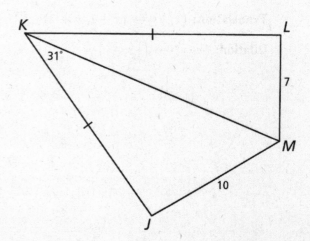

6.6 Self-Assessment

Use the scale to rate your understanding of the learning target and the success criteria.

| 1 | I do not understand yet. | 2 | I can do it with help. | 3 | I can do it on my own. | 4 | I can teach someone else. |

	Rating	Date
6.6 Inequalities in Two Triangles		
Learning Target: Understand inequalities in two triangles.	1 2 3 4	
I can explain the Hinge Theorem.	1 2 3 4	
I can compare measures in triangles.	1 2 3 4	
I can solve real-life problems using the Hinge Theorem.	1 2 3 4	

Name_____ Date_____

Chapter Self-Assessment

Use the scale to rate your understanding of the learning target and the success criteria.

1 I do not understand yet. **2** I can do it with help. **3** I can do it on my own. **4** I can teach someone else.

	Rating	Date
Chapter 6 Relationships Within Triangles		
Learning Target: Understand relationships within triangles.	1 2 3 4	
I can identify special segments in a triangle.	1 2 3 4	
I can use special segments in a triangle to solve problems.	1 2 3 4	
I can prove statements using special segments in a triangle.	1 2 3 4	
I can compare measures within triangles and between two triangles.	1 2 3 4	
6.1 Perpendicular and Angle Bisectors		
Learning Target: Use theorems about perpendicular and angle bisectors.	1 2 3 4	
I can identify a perpendicular bisector and an angle bisector.	1 2 3 4	
I can use theorems about bisectors to find measures in figures.	1 2 3 4	
I can write equations of perpendicular bisectors.	1 2 3 4	
6.2 Bisectors of Triangles		
Learning Target: Use bisectors of triangles.	1 2 3 4	
I can find the circumcenter and incenter of a triangle.	1 2 3 4	
I can circumscribe a circle about a triangle.	1 2 3 4	
I can inscribe a circle within a triangle.	1 2 3 4	
I can use points of concurrency to solve real-life problems.	1 2 3 4	
6.3 Medians and Altitudes of Triangles		
Learning Target: Use medians and altitudes of triangles.	1 2 3 4	
I can draw medians and altitudes of triangles.	1 2 3 4	
I can find the centroid of a triangle.	1 2 3 4	
I can find the orthocenter of a triangle.	1 2 3 4	

Chapter 6 Chapter Self-Assessment (continued)

	Rating	Date
6.4 The Triangle Midsegment Theorem		
Learning Target: Find and use midsegments of triangles.	1　2　3　4	
I can use midsegments of triangles in the coordinate plane to solve problems.	1　2　3　4	
I can solve real-life problems involving midsegments.	1　2　3　4	
6.5 Proof by Contradiction and Inequalities in One Triangle		
Learning Target: Write proofs by contradiction and understand inequalities in a triangle.	1　2　3　4	
I can write proofs by contradiction. **H**	1　2　3　4	
I can order the angles of a triangle given the side lengths.	1　2　3　4	
I can order the side lengths of a triangle given the angle measures.	1　2　3　4	
I can determine possible side lengths of triangles.	1　2　3　4	
6.6 Inequalities in Two Triangles		
Learning Target: Understand inequalities in two triangles.	1　2　3　4	
I can explain the Hinge Theorem.	1　2　3　4	
I can compare measures in triangles.	1　2　3　4	
I can solve real-life problems using the Hinge Theorem.	1　2　3　4	

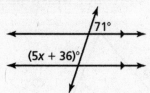

Chapter 6

B.E.S.T. Test Prep

1. What is the value of *x*?

71°

(5x + 36)°

2. Which point lies on the perpendicular bisector of the segment with endpoints $A(-3, 6)$ and $B(5, 2)$?

   Ⓐ (4, 10)

   Ⓑ (2, 2)

   Ⓒ (3, 3)

   Ⓓ (5, 6)

3. Point *D* is the centroid of $\triangle ABC$, and $DE = 6$. What is *CD*?

   Ⓐ 4

   Ⓑ 6

   Ⓒ 12

   Ⓓ 18

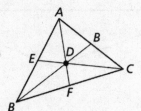

4. Point *N* is the incenter of $\triangle ABC$. $ND = 4x + 5$ and $NE = 8x - 3$. What is *NF*?

   Ⓐ 1

   Ⓑ 2

   Ⓒ 9

   Ⓓ 13

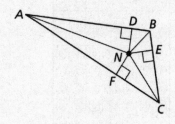

5. Which of the following are not corresponding parts of the congruent triangles?

   Ⓐ $\angle AEB \cong \angle CED$

   Ⓑ $\angle B \cong \angle C$

   Ⓒ $\overline{AB} \cong \overline{CD}$

   Ⓓ $\angle A \cong \angle C$

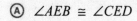

6. What is the perimeter of the triangle?

_____

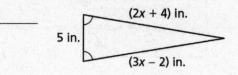

(2x + 4) in.

5 in.

(3x − 2) in.

7. What is *CE*?

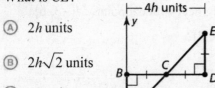

Ⓐ 2*h* units

Ⓑ 2*h*√2 units

Ⓒ 4*h* units

Ⓓ 4*h*√2 units

8. $\overline{DE}$ is a midsegment of △*ABC*. What is *BC*?

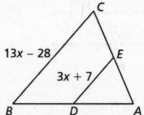

Ⓐ 6

Ⓑ 17.5

Ⓒ 35

Ⓓ 50

9. Three groups of hikers leave the same camp heading in different directions. Each group hikes 2.6 miles, then changes direction and hikes 3.2 miles. Group A starts due north and then turns 30° toward east. Group B starts due west and then turns 40° toward south. Group C starts due east and then turns 45° toward north. Which group is farther from camp?

Ⓐ Group A

Ⓑ Group B

Ⓒ Group C

Ⓓ All three groups are the same distance from camp.

10. △*FGH* ≅ △*JKL*. What is the value of *y*?

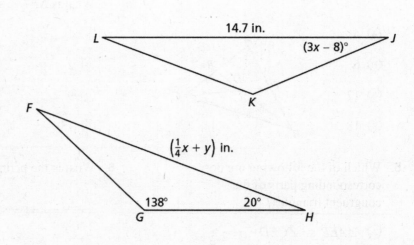

Chapter 6 **B.E.S.T. Test Prep** (continued)

11. Which of the following lists the angles of the triangle from smallest to largest?

Ⓐ ∠B, ∠C, ∠A

Ⓑ ∠A, ∠C, ∠B

Ⓒ ∠C, ∠B, ∠A

Ⓓ ∠B, ∠A, ∠C

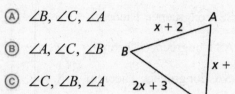

12. Which point of concurrency is point C?

Ⓐ circumcenter

Ⓑ incenter

Ⓒ centroid

Ⓓ orthocenter

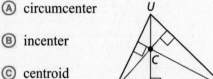

13. The line $y = -2x + 1$ is reflected in the line $y = 2$. Write the equation of the image.

_____

14. △XYZ has vertices $X(3, -2)$, $Y(5, 4)$, and $Z(-1, 6)$. Which of the following are the vertices of the midsegment triangle?

Ⓐ $(1, 2)$

Ⓑ $(-1, -3)$

Ⓒ $(2, -4)$

Ⓓ $(4, 1)$

Ⓔ $(3, -1)$

Ⓕ $(2, 5)$

15. In △DEF, which is a possible side length for $\overline{DF}$? Select all that apply.

Ⓐ 7.9

Ⓑ 8.2

Ⓒ 8.5

Ⓓ 8.9

Ⓔ 9.2

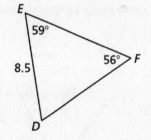

16. Which property does the statement "If $\overline{DE} \cong \overline{MN}$ and $\overline{MN} \cong \overline{XY}$, then $\overline{DE} \cong \overline{XY}$." illustrate?

Ⓐ Reflexive Property of Segment Congruence

Ⓑ Symmetric Property of Segment Congruence

Ⓒ Substitution Property of Equality

Ⓓ Transitive Property of Segment Congruence

Chapter 6 **B.E.S.T. Test Prep** (continued)

17. What is the perimeter of △*QTS*?

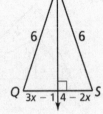

Ⓐ 13 units

Ⓑ 14 units

Ⓒ 16 units

Ⓓ 18 units

18. Which theorem can you use to prove that △*LMN* ≅ △*QPR*?

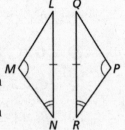

Ⓐ SSS Congruence Theorem

Ⓑ SAS Congruence Theorem

Ⓒ ASA Congruence Theorem

Ⓓ AAS Congruence Theorem

19. Which of the following statements is false?

Ⓐ The incenter of a triangle is equidistant from the sides of the triangle.

Ⓑ The circumcenter of a right triangle is on the triangle.

Ⓒ The incenter of an obtuse triangle is outside the triangle.

Ⓓ The circumcenter of a triangle is equidistance from the vertices of the triangle.

20. What is the angle of rotation that maps $\overline{CD}$ to $\overline{C''D''}$?

Ⓐ 26°

Ⓑ 52°

Ⓒ 78°

Ⓓ 104°

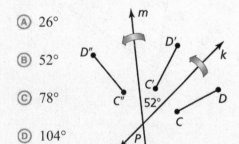

21. The midpoint of $\overline{RS}$ is $M(-7, 2)$. One endpoint is $S(-5, 6)$. What are the coordinates of endpoint R?

Ⓐ $(-9, -2)$

Ⓑ $(-3, 10)$

Ⓒ $(-6, 4)$

Ⓓ $(-1, -2)$

22. Which of the following is the inverse of the conditional statement?

Conditional statement If a polygon is an octagon, then it has eight sides.

Ⓐ If a polygon has eight sides, then it is an octagon.

Ⓑ If a polygon does not have eight sides, then it is not an octagon.

Ⓒ If a polygon is not an octagon, then it does not have eight sides.

Ⓓ A polygon is an octagon if and only if it has eight sides.

7.1   Review & Refresh

In Exercises 1 and 2, find the value of x.

1.

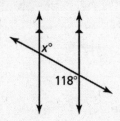

118°

2.

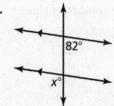

82°

x°

3.   Which is greater, $m\angle 1$ or $m\angle 2$? Explain your reasoning.

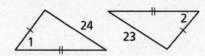

24

23

1

2

4.   Describe the possible lengths of the third side of a triangle with side lengths of 14 feet and 6 feet.

5.   Write an equation of the line that passes through $(8, -5)$ and is perpendicular to $y = -4x + 3$.

6.   Determine whether the polygon has line symmetry. If so, draw the line(s) of symmetry and describe any reflections that map the figure onto itself.

7. $\overline{MN}$ is a midsegment of $\triangle PQR$. Find the value of x.

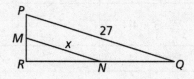

P

M

R   N

27

x

Q

7.1   Review & Refresh (continued)

8. The sum of the measures of the interior angles of a convex polygon is 2340°.
   Classify the polygon by the number of sides.

9. Find the measure of the exterior angle.

10. Find the value of x.

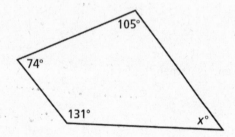

7.1   Self-Assessment

Use the scale to rate your understanding of the learning target and the success criteria.

| 1 | I do not understand yet. | 2 | I can do it with help. | 3 | I can do it on my own. | 4 | I can teach someone else. |

	Rating	Date
7.1 Angles of Polygons		
Learning Target: Find angle measures of polygons.	1 2 3 4	
I can find the sum of the interior angle measures of a polygon.	1 2 3 4	
I can find interior angle measures of polygons.	1 2 3 4	
I can find exterior angle measures of polygons.	1 2 3 4	

Name_____ Date_____

1. List the sides of $\triangle ABC$ in order from shortest to longest.

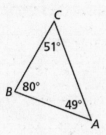

In Exercises 2–4, find the indicated measure in ▱QRST. Explain your reasoning.

2. QR

3. $\angle S$

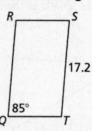

4. $\angle T$

5. Find the value of x.

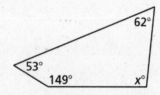

6. The coordinates of a point and its image after a reflection are shown. What is the line of reflection?

$$(-2, -9) \rightarrow (9, 2)$$

7. Find the coordinates of the intersection of the diagonals of ▱$ABCD$ with vertices $A(-7.5, 0)$, $B(-10.5, 7)$, $C(3, 7)$, and $D(6, 0)$.

7.2 Review & Refresh (continued)

8. Decide whether there is enough information to prove that $\ell \parallel m$. If so, state the theorem you can use.

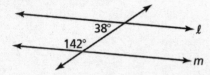

9. The hiking trail from A to B is shorter than the trail from C to D. The trail from A to D is the same length as the trail from C to B. What can you conclude about $\angle ADB$ and $\angle CBD$? Explain your reasoning.

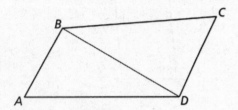

7.2 Self-Assessment

Use the scale to rate your understanding of the learning target and the success criteria.

| 1 | I do not understand yet. | 2 | I can do it with help. | 3 | I can do it on my own. | 4 | I can teach someone else. |

	Rating	Date
7.2 Properties of Parallelograms		
Learning Target: Prove and use properties of parallelograms.	1 2 3 4	
I can prove properties of parallelograms.	1 2 3 4	
I can use properties of parallelograms.	1 2 3 4	
I can solve problems involving parallelograms in the coordinate plane.	1 2 3 4	

Name_____ Date_____

1. Solve the equation $4 - 2y = 5 - 6x$ for y. Justify each step.

2. Find the value of x.

3. Find the distance between $X(-1, 5)$ and $Y(12, 2)$.

4. Three vertices of $\square ABCD$ are $A(-1, -4)$, $B(1, -1)$, and $C(-4, 1)$. Find the coordinates of the remaining vertex.

5. Graph the triangle with vertices $D(-1, 2)$, $E(1, 0)$, and $F(0, -1)$ and its image in the coordinate plane after a dilation with scale factor $k = 2$.

7.3 Review & Refresh (continued)

6. State which theorem you can use to show that the quadrilateral is a parallelogram.

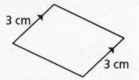

7. Place a rectangle with a length of 3ℓ units and a width of ℓ units in the coordinate plane. Find the length of the diagonal.

7.3 Self-Assessment

Use the scale to rate your understanding of the learning target and the success criteria.

1 I do not understand yet.	**2** I can do it with help.	**3** I can do it on my own.	**4** I can teach someone else.

	Rating	Date
7.3 Proving that a Quadrilateral Is a Parallelogram		
Learning Target: Prove that a quadrilateral is a parallelogram.	1 2 3 4	
I can identify features of a parallelogram.	1 2 3 4	
I can prove that a quadrilateral is a parallelogram.	1 2 3 4	
I can find missing lengths that make a quadrilateral a parallelogram.	1 2 3 4	
I can show that a quadrilateral in the coordinate plane is a parallelogram.	1 2 3 4	

7.4 Review & Refresh

In Exercises 1 and 2, use the translation.

$(x, y) \rightarrow (x - 5, y + 2)$

1. What is the image of $A(3, 4)$?   **2.** What is the preimage of $B'(-5, 6)$?

3. Rewrite the definition as a biconditional statement.

Definition A *midsegment of a triangle* is a segment that connects the midpoints of two sides of the triangle.

4. $\overline{DE}$ is a midsegment of $\triangle ABC$. Find the values of x and y.

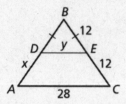

5. Find the values of x and y in the parallelogram.

6. Find the measure of each interior angle and each exterior angle of a regular 30-gon.

7.4 Review & Refresh (continued)

7. Find the perimeter and area of $\triangle XYZ$ with vertices $X(5, 1)$, $Y(-1, 1)$, and $Z(3, 2)$.

8. Decide whether you can use the given information to prove that $\triangle DEF \cong \triangle QRS$. Explain your reasoning.

$\angle D \cong \angle Q, \angle F \cong \angle S, \overline{EF} \cong \overline{RS}$

9. Find the length of $\overline{AB}$. Explain your reasoning.

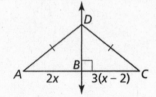

7.4 Self-Assessment

Use the scale to rate your understanding of the learning target and the success criteria.

| 1 | I do not understand yet. | 2 | I can do it with help. | 3 | I can do it on my own. | 4 | I can teach someone else. |

	Rating	Date
7.4 Properties of Special Parallelograms		
Learning Target: Explain the properties of special parallelograms.	1 2 3 4	
I can identify special quadrilaterals.	1 2 3 4	
I can explain how special parallelograms are related.	1 2 3 4	
I can find missing measures of special parallelograms.	1 2 3 4	
I can identify special parallelograms in a coordinate plane.	1 2 3 4	

7.5 Review & Refresh

1. Decide whether enough information is given to prove that $\triangle RUT$ and $\triangle RUS$ are congruent using the HL Congruence Theorem.

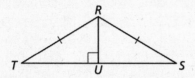

2. Find the distance from $(6, -1)$ to the line $y = x + 7$.

3. Classify the quadrilateral.

4. Find DB in $\square ABCD$. Explain your reasoning.

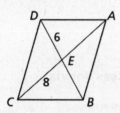

5. State which theorem you can use to show that the quadrilateral is a parallelogram.

50°   130°

130°   50°

6. Find the perimeter of the outer frame of the bridge.

35 ft

252 ft

7.5 Review & Refresh (continued)

7. Graph $\overline{EF}$ with endpoints $E(2, 7)$ and $F(1, 4)$ and its image after a reflection in the y-axis, followed by a translation 3 units down.

8. Find the measure of each angle in the isosceles trapezoid.

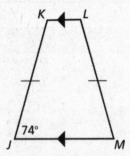

7.5 Self-Assessment

Use the scale to rate your understanding of the learning target and the success criteria.

| 1 | I do not understand yet. | 2 | I can do it with help. | 3 | I can do it on my own. | 4 | I can teach someone else. |

	Rating	Date
7.5 Properties of Trapezoids and Kites		
Learning Target: Use properties of trapezoids and kites to find measures.	1 2 3 4	
I can identify trapezoids and kites.	1 2 3 4	
I can use properties of trapezoids and kites to solve problems.	1 2 3 4	
I can find the length of the midsegment of a trapezoid.	1 2 3 4	
I can explain the hierarchy of quadrilaterals.	1 2 3 4	

Chapter Self-Assessment

Use the scale to rate your understanding of the learning target and the success criteria.

1 I do not understand yet.   **2** I can do it with help.   **3** I can do it on my own.   **4** I can teach someone else.

	Rating	Date
Chapter 7 Quadrilaterals and Other Polygons		
Learning Target: Understand quadrilaterals and other polygons.	1 2 3 4	
I can find angles of a polygon.	1 2 3 4	
I can describe properties of parallelograms.	1 2 3 4	
I can use properties of parallelograms to solve problems.	1 2 3 4	
I can justify why a figure is a special quadrilateral.	1 2 3 4	
7.1 Angles of Polygons		
Learning Target: Find angle measures of polygons.	1 2 3 4	
I can find the sum of the interior angle measures of a polygon.	1 2 3 4	
I can find interior angle measures of polygons.	1 2 3 4	
I can find exterior angle measures of polygons.	1 2 3 4	
7.2 Properties of Parallelograms		
Learning Target: Prove and use properties of parallelograms.	1 2 3 4	
I can prove properties of parallelograms.	1 2 3 4	
I can use properties of parallelograms.	1 2 3 4	
I can solve problems involving parallelograms in the coordinate plane.	1 2 3 4	
7.3 Proving that a Quadrilateral Is a Parallelogram		
Learning Target: Prove that a quadrilateral is a parallelogram.	1 2 3 4	
I can identify features of a parallelogram.	1 2 3 4	
I can prove that a quadrilateral is a parallelogram.	1 2 3 4	
I can find missing lengths that make a quadrilateral a parallelogram.	1 2 3 4	
I can show that a quadrilateral in the coordinate plane is a parallelogram.	1 2 3 4	

Chapter 7 Chapter Self-Assessment (continued)

	Rating	Date
7.4 Properties of Special Parallelograms		
Learning Target: Explain the properties of special parallelograms.	1 2 3 4	
I can identify special quadrilaterals.	1 2 3 4	
I can explain how special parallelograms are related.	1 2 3 4	
I can find missing measures of special parallelograms.	1 2 3 4	
I can identify special parallelograms in a coordinate plane.	1 2 3 4	
7.5 Properties of Trapezoids and Kites		
Learning Target: Use properties of trapezoids and kites to find measures.	1 2 3 4	
I can identify trapezoids and kites.	1 2 3 4	
I can use properties of trapezoids and kites to solve problems.	1 2 3 4	
I can find the length of the midsegment of a trapezoid.	1 2 3 4	
I can explain the hierarchy of quadrilaterals.	1 2 3 4	

Chapter 7 **B.E.S.T. Test Prep**

1. What is *CD*?

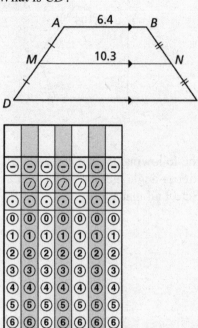

2. What is the measure (in degrees) of the exterior angle?

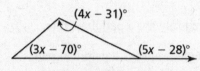

3. What is the value of *x*?

Ⓐ 6.25

Ⓑ 10

Ⓒ 22.5

Ⓓ 45

(6x − 15)°

4. Which reason justifies the third statement in the proof?

Ⓐ Corresponding parts of congruent triangles are congruent.

Ⓑ Definition of congruent angles

Ⓒ Vertical Angles Congruence Theorem

Ⓓ Definition of angle bisector

Given $\overline{AC} \cong \overline{DE}$, $\angle C \cong \angle E$, $\angle A \cong \angle D$

Prove $\angle ABC \cong \angle DBE$

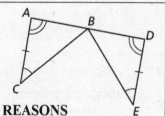

STATEMENTS	REASONS
1. $\overline{AC} \cong \overline{DE}$, $\angle C \cong \angle E$, $\angle A \cong \angle D$	1. Given
2. $\triangle ABC \cong \triangle DBE$	2. ASA Congruence Theorem
3. $\angle ABC \cong \angle DBE$	3.

Chapter 7

B.E.S.T. Test Prep (continued)

5. Which of the following statements is false?

   Ⓐ A square is always a rhombus.

   Ⓑ A square is always a parallelogram.

   Ⓒ A rectangle is always a parallelogram.

   Ⓓ A parallelogram is always a rhombus.

6. What is $m\angle C$?

   Ⓐ 71°

   Ⓑ 109°

   Ⓒ 116°

   Ⓓ 161°

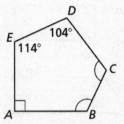

7. Three vertices of a parallelogram are $(-3, 1)$, $(-1, 4)$, and $(5, 1)$. Which of the following could be the fourth vertex of The parallelogram? Select all that apply.

   Ⓐ $(5, -1)$

   Ⓑ $(-1, -2)$

   Ⓒ $(3, -2)$

   Ⓓ $(3, 4)$

   Ⓔ $(-9, 4)$

   Ⓕ $(7, 4)$

8. Which of the following angle measures are possible exterior angle measures of a regular polygon? Select all that apply.

   Ⓐ 8°

   Ⓑ 12°

   Ⓒ 54°

   Ⓓ 108°

   Ⓔ 120°

   Ⓕ 162°

9. What is the value of x?

   Ⓐ 3

   Ⓑ 4

   Ⓒ 6

   Ⓓ 8

$2x + y$ 13 $x + 3y$ 11

10. $\triangle JKL$ has vertices $J(-4, 5)$, $K(2, 3)$, and $L(0, 1)$. What is the perimeter of its midsegment triangle?

_____

11. What is the most specific name for the quadrilateral with vertices (6, 8), (5, 6), (9, 7), and (10, 9)?

Ⓐ parallelogram

Ⓑ rhombus

Ⓒ rectangle

Ⓓ square

12. Which of the following does not provide enough information to prove that the quadrilateral is a parallelogram?

Ⓐ $\overline{DE} \cong \overline{FG}, \overline{EF} \cong \overline{GD}$

Ⓑ $\overline{EF} \cong \overline{GD}, \overline{EF} \parallel \overline{GD}$

Ⓒ $\overline{DE} \parallel \overline{FG}, \overline{EF} \parallel \overline{GD}$

Ⓓ $\overline{EF} \cong \overline{GD}, \overline{DE} \parallel \overline{FG}$

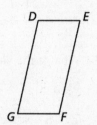

13. What can you conclude from the diagram?

Ⓐ $EH = GH$

Ⓑ $EH < GH$

Ⓒ $EH > GH$

Ⓓ No conclusion can be made.

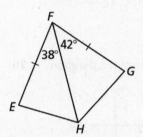

14. What is the distance (in units) between the point (3, 2) and its image after the composition?

Translation: $(x, y) \rightarrow (x + 7, y - 1)$
Translation: $(x, y) \rightarrow (x - 2, y + 13)$

15. $\triangle ABC$ has vertices $A(-5, 8)$, $B(7, 8)$, and $C(7, 3)$. What is the difference (in units) of the perimeter of $\triangle ABC$ and the perimeter of its image after the similarity transformation?

Reflection: in the y-axis

Dilation: $(x, y) \rightarrow (3x, 3y)$

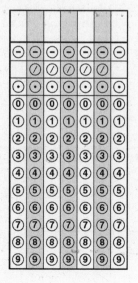

Chapter 7 **B.E.S.T. Test Prep** (continued)

16. What are the coordinates of the orthocenter of $\triangle WXY$ with vertices $W(2, 7)$, $X(3, 4)$, and $Y(6, 7)$?

_____

17. What is the value of y?

Ⓐ 4

Ⓑ 10

Ⓒ 28

Ⓓ 30

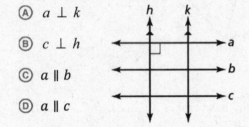

18. What is the value of x?

Ⓐ 6.25

Ⓑ 10.625

Ⓒ 11.875

Ⓓ 45

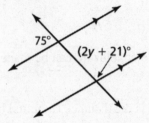

19. What can you conclude from the diagram?

Ⓐ $a \perp k$

Ⓑ $c \perp h$

Ⓒ $a \parallel b$

Ⓓ $a \parallel c$

20. What is the value of y?

Ⓐ 27

Ⓑ 42

Ⓒ 75

Ⓓ 105

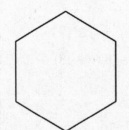

21. What rotations map the polygon onto itself? Select all that apply.

Ⓐ 30°

Ⓑ 60°

Ⓒ 90°

Ⓓ 120°

Ⓔ 180°

Ⓕ The polygon does not have rotational symmetry.

22. Which congruence statement is correct?

Ⓐ $\triangle ABC \cong \triangle MNP$

Ⓑ $\triangle ACB \cong \triangle MPN$

Ⓒ $\triangle CAB \cong \triangle NMP$

Ⓓ $\triangle BCA \cong \triangle PMN$

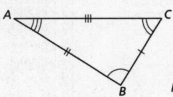

Name_____ Date_____

8.1 Review & Refresh

In Exercises 1 and 2, find the value of *x*.

1.

2.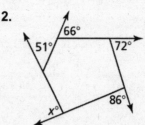

3. In rectangle $WXYZ$, $WY = 9x - 25$ and $XZ = 19 - 2x$. Find the lengths of the diagonals of $WXYZ$.

4. Find the values of *x* and *y* that make the quadrilateral a parallelogram.

In Exercises 5 and 6, factor the polynomial.

5. $-5x^2 + 9x + 18$

6. $x^3 - 2x^2 - 3x + 6$

7. The two triangles are similar. Find the value of *x*.

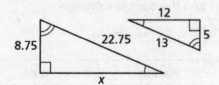

8. Tell whether the table of values represents a *linear*, an *exponential*, or a *quadratic* function.

x	−1	0	1	2	3
y	3	−1	3	15	35

In Exercises 9 and 10, solve the equation.

9. $3^{2(x+1)} = \left(\dfrac{1}{81}\right)^{x-5}$

10. $4x^2 - 11 = 7$

8.1 Review & Refresh (continued)

11. The incenter of $\triangle ABC$ is point N, $NZ = 7x + 1$, and $NX = 2x + 6$. Find NY.

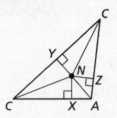

12. Rhombus A is similar to rhombus B. Rhombus A has an area of 32 square feet. Rhombus B has an area of 98 square feet and a side length of 21 feet. Find the perimeter of rhombus A.

13. Tell whether two rectangles are *always*, *sometimes*, or *never* similar.

8.1 Self-Assessment

Use the scale to rate your understanding of the learning target and the success criteria.

| 1 | I do not understand yet. | 2 | I can do it with help. | 3 | I can do it on my own. | 4 | I can teach someone else. |

	Rating	Date
8.1 Similar Polygons		
Learning Target: Understand the relationship between similar polygons.	1 2 3 4	
I can use similarity statements.	1 2 3 4	
I can find corresponding lengths in similar polygons.	1 2 3 4	
I can find perimeters and areas of similar polygons.	1 2 3 4	
I can decide whether polygons are similar.	1 2 3 4	

8.2 Review & Refresh

1. Decide whether enough information is given to prove that the triangles are congruent. If so, state the theorem you can use.

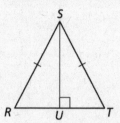

2. Determine whether the triangles are similar. If they are, write a similarity statement. Explain your reasoning.

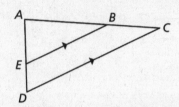

3. A bolt has a head shaped like a regular hexagon. Find the measure of each (a) interior angle and (b) exterior angle.

4. Find $m\angle N$.

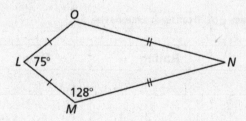

5. In the diagram, $QRST \sim WXYZ$. The area of $WXYZ$ is 64 square feet. Find the area of $QRST$.

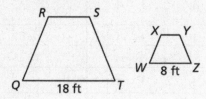

8.2° Review & Refresh (continued)

6. Decide whether ☐ABCD with vertices A(−3, 4), B(−1, 1), C(2, 3), and D(0, 6) is a *rectangle*, a *rhombus*, or a *square*. Give all names that apply.

In Exercises 7–12, use the diagram to complete the statement.

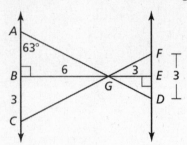

7. $m\angle AGB =$ ☐

8. $m\angle EGD =$ ☐

9. $m\angle BCG =$ ☐

10. $AB =$ ☐

11. $FE =$ ☐

12. $\triangle AGC \sim$ ☐

8.2 Self-Assessment

Use the scale to rate your understanding of the learning target and the success criteria.

| 1 | I do not understand yet. | 2 | I can do it with help. | 3 | I can do it on my own. | 4 | I can teach someone else. |

	Rating	Date
8.2 Proving Triangle Similarity by AA		
Learning Target: Understand and use the Angle-Angle Similarity Theorem.	1 2 3 4	
I can use similarity transformations to prove the Angle-Angle Similarity Theorem. **H**	1 2 3 4	
I can use angle measures of triangles to determine whether triangles are similar.	1 2 3 4	
I can prove triangle similarity using the Angle-Angle Similarity Theorem.	1 2 3 4	
I can solve real-life problems using similar triangles.	1 2 3 4	

8.3 Review & Refresh

1. A xylophone consists of wooden bars. Each bar is parallel to the bar directly to the right. Explain why the longest bar is parallel to the shortest bar.

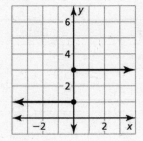

2. Show that $\triangle ABD$ and $\triangle CBA$ are similar. Then write a similarity statement.

3. Find the coordinates of point P along the directed line segment AB with vertices $A(-1, 1)$ and $B(7, 3)$ so that the ratio of AP to PB is 1 to 3.

4. A triangle has side lengths of 7 meters and 16 meters. Describe the possible lengths of the third side.

5. Determine whether the graph represents a function. Explain.

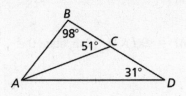

6. Write an equation of the perpendicular bisector of the segment with endpoints $T(4, 9)$ and $U(2, 3)$.

8.3 Review & Refresh (continued)

In Exercises 7 and 8, find $m\angle C$.

7.

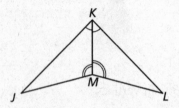

8.

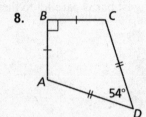

9. Decide whether enough information is given to prove that $\triangle JKM \cong \triangle LKM$. If so, state the theorem you can use.

8.3 Self-Assessment

Use the scale to rate your understanding of the learning target and the success criteria.

| 1 | I do not understand yet. | 2 | I can do it with help. | 3 | I can do it on my own. | 4 | I can teach someone else. |

	Rating	Date
8.3 Proving Triangle Similarity by SSS and SAS		
Learning Target: Understand and use additional triangle similarity theorems.	1 2 3 4	
I can use the SSS and SAS Similarity Theorems to determine whether triangles are similar.	1 2 3 4	
I can use similar triangles to prove theorems about slopes of parallel and perpendicular lines.	1 2 3 4	

8.4 Review & Refresh

1. Graph $\triangle JKL$ with vertices $J(-1, 2)$, $K(0, 1)$, and $L(-2, -1)$ and its image after the similarity transformation.

Dilation: $(x, y) \rightarrow (3x, 3y)$

Reflection: in the x-axis

2. You are building a birdhouse with the triangular front shown. You want to make the entrance the same distance from each side of the triangular front. Determine the location of the entrance.

3. Find the value of x when $\triangle ABC \sim \triangle RST$.

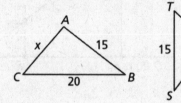

4. Solve the equation $A = \dfrac{1}{2}h(b_1 + b_2)$ for b_1.

5. Show that the triangles are similar. Write a similarity statement.

Name _____ Date _____

6. Find the value of x.

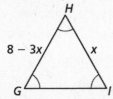

$8 - 3x$ x

In Exercises 7 and 8, find the value of the variable.

7.

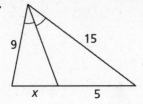

8.

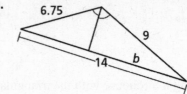

9. The diagram shows the skyline of a city. Find the distance between point E and point F for which $\overline{BE} \parallel \overline{CF}$. Explain your reasoning.

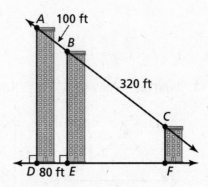

8.4 **Self-Assessment**

Use the scale to rate your understanding of the learning target and the success criteria.

| **1** | I do not understand yet. | **2** | I can do it with help. | **3** | I can do it on my own. | **4** | I can teach someone else. |

	Rating	Date
8.4 Proportionality Theorems		
Learning Target: Understand and use proportionality theorems.	1 2 3 4	
I can use proportionality theorems to find lengths in triangles.	1 2 3 4	
I can find lengths when two transversals intersect three parallel lines.	1 2 3 4	
I can find lengths when a ray bisects an angle of a triangle.	1 2 3 4	

Name_____ Date_____

Chapter Self-Assessment

Use the scale to rate your understanding of the learning target and the success criteria.

1 I do not understand yet. **2** I can do it with help. **3** I can do it on my own. **4** I can teach someone else.

	Rating	Date
Chapter 8 Similarity		
Learning Target: Understand similarity.	1 2 3 4	
I can identify corresponding parts of similar polygons.	1 2 3 4	
I can find and use scale factors in similar polygons.	1 2 3 4	
I can prove triangles are similar.	1 2 3 4	
I can use proportionality theorems to solve problems.	1 2 3 4	
8.1 Similar Polygons		
Learning Target: Understand the relationship between similar polygons.	1 2 3 4	
I can use similarity statements.	1 2 3 4	
I can find corresponding lengths in similar polygons.	1 2 3 4	
I can find perimeters and areas of similar polygons.	1 2 3 4	
I can decide whether polygons are similar.	1 2 3 4	
8.2 Proving Triangle Similarity by AA		
Learning Target: Understand and use the Angle-Angle Similarity Theorem.	1 2 3 4	
I can use similarity transformations to prove the Angle-Angle Similarity Theorem. **H**	1 2 3 4	
I can use angle measures of triangles to determine whether triangles are similar.	1 2 3 4	
I can prove triangle similarity using the Angle-Angle Similarity Theorem.	1 2 3 4	
I can solve real-life problems using similar triangles.	1 2 3 4	
8.3 Proving Triangle Similarity by SSS and SAS		
Learning Target: Understand and use additional triangle similarity theorems.	1 2 3 4	
I can use the SSS and SAS Similarity Theorems to determine whether triangles are similar.	1 2 3 4	
I can use similar triangles to prove theorems about slopes of parallel and perpendicular lines.	1 2 3 4	

Name _____ Date _____

	Rating	Date
8.4 Proportionality Theorems		
Learning Target: Understand and use proportionality theorems.	1 2 3 4	
I can use proportionality theorems to find lengths in triangles.	1 2 3 4	
I can find lengths when two transversals intersect three parallel lines.	1 2 3 4	
I can find lengths when a ray bisects an angle of a triangle.	1 2 3 4	

Chapter 8
B.E.S.T. Test Prep

1. Rectangle A is similar to rectangle B. Rectangle A has side lengths of 8 and 20. Rectangle B has a side length of 10. What are the possible values for the length of the other side of rectangle B? Select all that apply.

   Ⓐ 4   Ⓒ 25

   Ⓑ 16   Ⓓ 40

2. Which of the following statements is false?

   Ⓐ $AC < BC$

   Ⓑ $AB < AC + BC$

   Ⓒ $BC > AB$

   Ⓓ $\triangle ABC$ is scalene.

   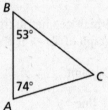

3. In the diagram, $\dfrac{AC}{DC} = \dfrac{BC}{EC}$. Which of the following statements is false?

   Ⓐ $\overline{AB} \parallel \overline{DE}$

   Ⓑ $\triangle ABC \sim \triangle DEC$

   Ⓒ $\angle A \cong \angle D$

   Ⓓ $\angle ABC \cong \angle EDC$

   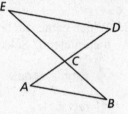

4. In $\square PQRS$, the ratio of QR to RS is 3 to 2. The perimeter of $\square PQRS$ is 70 units. What is the length, in units, of PS?

5. A tree casts a shadow that is 90 feet long. A person standing nearby who is 5 feet 6 inches casts a shadow that is 72 inches long. How tall, in feet, is the tree?

6. What are the coordinates of the circumcenter of the triangle with vertices $(-2, -1)$, $(-6, -1)$, and $(-6, 11)$.

_____

Chapter 8

B.E.S.T. Test Prep (continued)

7. Which figure is stable?

Ⓐ

Ⓒ

Ⓑ

Ⓓ

8. Which name can be used to classify the quadrilateral? Select all that apply.

Ⓐ parallelogram

Ⓑ rectangle

Ⓒ rhombus

Ⓓ trapezoid

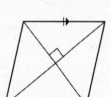

9. Which geometric figure illustrates the graph of $2x + 3 \leq 7$?

Ⓐ point

Ⓑ line

Ⓒ line segment

Ⓓ ray

10. What is the scale factor from $\triangle ABC$ to $\triangle DEF$?

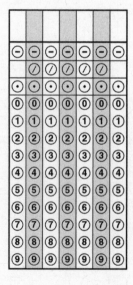

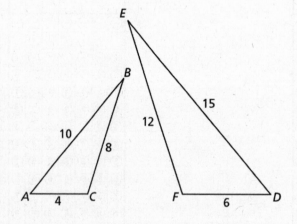

Chapter 8

B.E.S.T. Test Prep (continued)

11. What is AC?

Ⓐ $5\frac{1}{4}$

Ⓑ 12

Ⓒ $12\frac{1}{4}$

Ⓓ $16\frac{1}{3}$

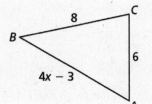

12. What is the value of z?

Ⓐ 1.8

Ⓑ 4

Ⓒ 5

Ⓓ 7.2

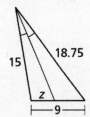

13. Figure X is similar to figure Y. Figure X has a perimeter of 22 inches and an area of 80 square inches. Figure Y has a perimeter of 55 inches. What is the area of figure Y?

Ⓐ 12.8 square inches

Ⓒ 200 square inches

Ⓑ 32 square inches

Ⓓ 500 square inches

14. What value of x makes $\triangle ABC \sim \triangle XYZ$?

Ⓐ 3

Ⓑ 4

Ⓒ 9

Ⓓ 10

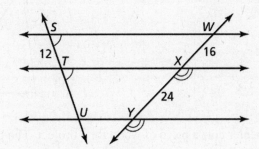

15. What is TU?

Ⓐ 8

Ⓑ 18

Ⓒ 20

Ⓓ 32

16. A reflection in a line maps point $B(3, -1)$ to point $B'(11, -1)$. What is the equation of the line of reflection?

_____

Chapter 8 **B.E.S.T. Test Prep** (continued)

17. Which of the following quadrilaterals does not have perpendicular diagonals?

Ⓐ rectangle

Ⓑ rhombus

Ⓒ square

Ⓓ kite

18. Which of the following statements illustrates the Transitive Property of Equality?

Ⓐ If $a = b$ and $b = c$, then $a = c$.

Ⓑ If $x = y$, then $y = x$.

Ⓒ $a = a$

Ⓓ If $AB = CD$, then $CD = AB$.

19. In a triangle, $m\angle P = 47°$ and $m\angle Q = 103°$. In another triangle, $m\angle S = (x - 7)°$ and $m\angle T = (y + 4)°$. For which of the following values of x and y are the two triangles similar?

Ⓐ $x = 37$, $y = 110$

Ⓑ $x = 110$, $y = 99$

Ⓒ $x = 54$, $y = 26$

Ⓓ $x = 47$, $y = 103$

20. The shortest side of a triangle similar to $\triangle FGH$ is 10 units long. What is the sum of the other side lengths of the triangle?

Ⓐ 12.5

Ⓑ 15

Ⓒ 20

Ⓓ 27.5

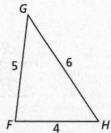

21. A carpenter cuts a piece of wood for a project. The piece of wood can be represented in the coordinate plane by a triangle with vertices $L(5, -1)$, $M(9, 7)$, and $N(1, 3)$. What type of triangle is $\triangle LMN$?

Ⓐ equilateral

Ⓑ isosceles

Ⓒ scalene

Name_____ Date_____

9.1 Review & Refresh

In Exercises 1 and 2, simplify the expression.

1. $\dfrac{18}{\sqrt{3}}$

2. $\dfrac{5}{3 + \sqrt{2}}$

3. $ABCD$ is an isosceles trapezoid, where $\overline{AB} \parallel \overline{CD}$, $\overline{AD} \cong \overline{BC}$, and $m\angle C = 105°$. Find $m\angle A$, $m\angle B$, and $m\angle D$.

4. A company creates a triangular shelf, as shown. Determine whether $\triangle JKL \sim \triangle MKN$. Explain.

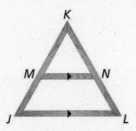

5. Tell whether the triangle is a right triangle.

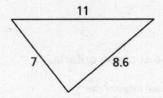

6. Show that the triangles are similar and write a similarity statement.

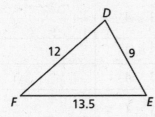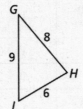

9.1 **Review & Refresh** (continued)

7. Graph $\triangle ABC$ with vertices $A(1, 3)$, $B(-2, 0)$, and $C(-1, 2)$ and its image after a reflection in the line $y = x$.

8. Find the value of x. Then tell whether the side lengths form a Pythagorean triple.

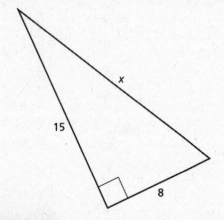

9.1 **Self-Assessment**

Use the scale to rate your understanding of the learning target and the success criteria.

| 1 | I do not understand yet. | 2 | I can do it with help. | 3 | I can do it on my own. | 4 | I can teach someone else. |

	Rating	Date
9.1 The Pythagorean Theorem		
Learning Target: Understand and apply the Pythagorean Theorem.	1 2 3 4	
I can list common Pythagorean triples.	1 2 3 4	
I can find missing side lengths of right triangles.	1 2 3 4	
I can classify a triangle as acute, right, or obtuse given its side lengths.	1 2 3 4	

9.2 Review & Refresh

1. In the diagram, $\triangle ABC \sim \triangle XYZ$. Find the value of x.

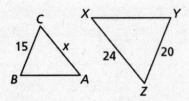

2. Determine whether segments with lengths of 4.9 meters, 7.0 meters, and 8.5 meters form a triangle. If so, is the triangle *acute*, *right*, or *obtuse*?

3. Find the values of x and y. Write your answers in simplest form.

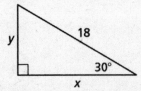

4. The endpoints of $\overline{JK}$ are $J(-4, 3)$ and $K(8, -1)$. Find the coordinates of the midpoint M.

5. Determine whether the polygons with the given vertices are congruent. Use transformations to explain your reasoning.

$A(2, 5)$, $B(4, 6)$, $C(5, 1)$ and $D(-1, 4)$, $E(1, 5)$, $F(2, 0)$

6. Which tiles, if any, are similar? Explain.

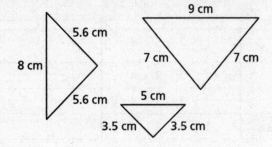

9.2 Review & Refresh (continued)

7. Three vertices of $\square WXYZ$ are $W(-3, 4)$, $Y(7, 3)$, and $Z(1, 6)$. Find the coordinates of vertex X.

8. Rewrite the definition as a biconditional statement.

   Definition A: trapezoid is a quadrilateral with exactly one pair of parallel sides.

9. Find the value of x. Write your answer in simplest form.

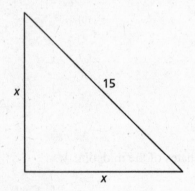

9.2 Self-Assessment

Use the scale to rate your understanding of the learning target and the success criteria.

| 1 | I do not understand yet. | 2 | I can do it with help. | 3 | I can do it on my own. | 4 | I can teach someone else. |

	Rating	Date
9.2 Special Right Triangles		
Learning Target: Understand and use special right triangles.	1 2 3 4	
I can find side lengths in 45°-45°-90° triangles.	1 2 3 4	
I can find side lengths in 30°-60°-90° triangles.	1 2 3 4	
I can use special right triangles to solve real-life problems.	1 2 3 4	

9.3 Review & Refresh

1. $\overline{MN}$ is a midsegment of $\triangle XYZ$. Find the value of x.

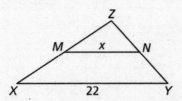

2. Find the geometric mean of 6 and 24.

3. Find the lengths of the diagonals of rectangle $ABCD$ given $AC = 6x - 5$ and $BD = 2x + 11$.

4. How tall is the tent?

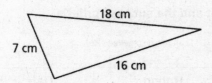

5. Tell whether the triangle is a right triangle.

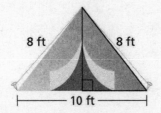

6. Find the value of y.

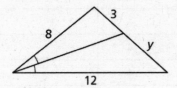

9.3 Review & Refresh (continued)

7. Determine whether the triangles are similar. If so, write a similarity statement. Explain your reasoning.

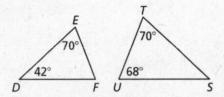

8. Graph $\triangle ABC$ with vertices $A(5, 1)$, $B(3, -2)$, and $C(2, 0)$ and its image after a translation 4 units up, followed by a reflection in the x-axis.

9. Identify the similar triangles.

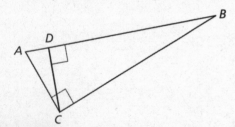

9.3 Self-Assessment

Use the scale to rate your understanding of the learning target and the success criteria.

| 1 | I do not understand yet. | 2 | I can do it with help. | 3 | I can do it on my own. | 4 | I can teach someone else. |

	Rating	Date
9.3 Similar Right Triangles		
Learning Target: Use proportional relationships in right triangles.	1 2 3 4	
I can explain the Right Triangle Similarity Theorem.	1 2 3 4	
I can find the geometric mean of two numbers.	1 2 3 4	
I can find missing dimensions in right triangles.	1 2 3 4	

9.4 Review & Refresh

1. Find the value of x. Tell whether the side lengths form a Pythagorean triple.

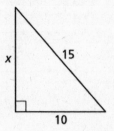

2. Find the geometric mean of 12 and 16.

3. Find the area of the polygon with vertices $(3, 1)$, $(1, 2)$, and $(3, 7)$.

4. Graph $\overline{MN}$ with endpoints $M(4, -3)$ and $N(-1, 2)$ and its image after a reflection in the y-axis, followed by a 90° rotation about the origin.

5. Find the coordinates of the circumcenter of the triangle with vertices $X(-4, 1)$, $Y(-2, 3)$, and $Z(2, -1)$.

9.4 Review & Refresh (continued)

In Exercises 6−9, find the value of *x*.

6.

7.
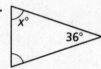

8.
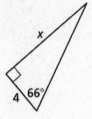

9.
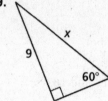

10. The vertical boards of a fence are parallel. Find $m\angle 2$.

9.4 Self-Assessment

Use the scale to rate your understanding of the learning target and the success criteria.

| 1 | I do not understand yet. | 2 | I can do it with help. | 3 | I can do it on my own. | 4 | I can teach someone else. |

	Rating	Date
9.4 The Tangent Ratio		
Learning Target: Understand and use the tangent ratio.	1 2 3 4	
I can explain the tangent ratio.	1 2 3 4	
I can find tangent ratios.	1 2 3 4	
I can use tangent ratios to solve real-life problems.	1 2 3 4	

Name_____ Date _____

In Exercises 1 and 2, find the value of *x*. Tell whether the side lengths form a Pythagorean triple.

1.

2.
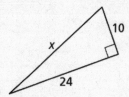

3. Write cos 71° in terms of sine.

4. Find the value of *x*.

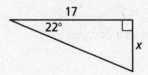

5. Find the measure of each interior angle and each exterior angle of a regular 25-gon.

6. Identify the similar right triangles. Then find the value of *x*.

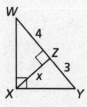

7. Find the values of *x* and *y*. Write your answers in simplest form.

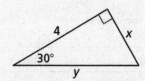

8. The polygons are congruent. Find the values of *x* and *y*.

9.5 Review & Refresh (continued)

9. Draw a rectangle with a length of 12 units and a width of 2 units in a coordinate plane. Find the length of a diagonal.

10. Given the points $A(6, -1)$ and $B(0, 7)$, find the coordinates of point P along the directed line segment AB so the ratio of AP to PB is 3 to 2.

11. Find $\sin D$, $\sin E$, $\cos D$, and $\cos E$. Write each answer as a fraction and as a decimal.

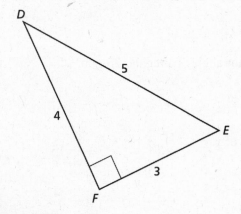

9.5 Self-Assessment

Use the scale to rate your understanding of the learning target and the success criteria.

| 1 | I do not understand yet. | 2 | I can do it with help. | 3 | I can do it on my own. | 4 | I can teach someone else. |

	Rating	Date
9.5 The Sine and Cosine Ratios		
Learning Target: Understand and use the sine and cosine ratios.	1 2 3 4	
I can explain the sine and cosine ratios.	1 2 3 4	
I can find sine and cosine ratios.	1 2 3 4	
I can use sine and cosine ratios to solve real-life problems.	1 2 3 4	

9.6 **Review & Refresh**

In Exercises 1–4, find the value of x.

1.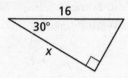

2.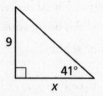

3.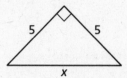

4.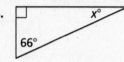

5. A triangle has one side length of 5 inches and another side length of 11 inches. Describe the possible lengths of the third side.

6. Quadrilateral $ABCD$ has vertices $A(7, 1)$, $B(5, 3)$, $C(4, 6)$, and $D(6, 4)$. Quadrilateral $EFGH$ has vertices $E(3, 3)$, $F(5, 1)$, $G(8, 0)$, and $H(6, 2)$. Are the two quadrilaterals congruent? Use transformations to explain your reasoning.

7. Solve $-4 = \sqrt[3]{11x - 20}$.

8. Find the values of x and y.

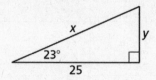

9. State which theorem you can use to show that the quadrilateral is a parallelogram.

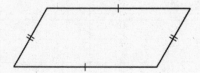

Name _____ Date _____

10. You draw a map of the street from your home to the post office on a coordinate plane. The post office is exactly halfway between your home and your school. Your home is located at the point $(3, 7)$ and the post office is located at the point $(5, 3)$. What point represents the location of your school?

In Exercises 11 and 12, solve the triangle.

11.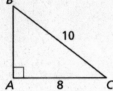

12.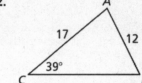

13.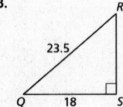

14.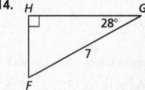

9.6 Self-Assessment

Use the scale to rate your understanding of the learning target and the success criteria.

| 1 | I do not understand yet. | 2 | I can do it with help. | 3 | I can do it on my own. | 4 | I can teach someone else. |

	Rating	Date
H 9.6 Law of Sines and Law of Cosines		
Learning Target: Find unknown side lengths and angle measures of acute and obtuse triangles.	1 2 3 4	
I can find areas of triangles using formulas that involve sines.	1 2 3 4	
I can use inverse trigonometric ratios to approximate angle measures.	1 2 3 4	
I can find unknown measures in triangles using the Law of Sines.	1 2 3 4	
I can find unknown measures in triangles using the Law of Cosines.	1 2 3 4	

Name_____ Date_____

Chapter 9   Chapter Self-Assessment

Use the scale to rate your understanding of the learning target and the success criteria.

1 I do not understand yet.   **2** I can do it with help.   **3** I can do it on my own.   **4** I can teach someone else.

	Rating	Date
Chapter 9 Right Triangles and Trigonometry		
Learning Target: Understand right triangles and trigonometry.	1 2 3 4	
I can use the Pythagorean Theorem to solve problems.	1 2 3 4	
I can find side lengths in special right triangles.	1 2 3 4	
I can explain how similar triangles are used with trigonometric ratios.	1 2 3 4	
I can use trigonometric ratios to solve problems.	1 2 3 4	
9.1 The Pythagorean Theorem		
Learning Target: Understand and apply the Pythagorean Theorem.	1 2 3 4	
I can list common Pythagorean triples.	1 2 3 4	
I can find missing side lengths of right triangles.	1 2 3 4	
I can classify a triangle as acute, right, or obtuse given its side lengths.	1 2 3 4	
9.2 Special Right Triangles		
Learning Target: Understand and use special right triangles.	1 2 3 4	
I can find side lengths in 45°-45°-90° triangles.	1 2 3 4	
I can find side lengths in 30°-60°-90° triangles.	1 2 3 4	
I can use special right triangles to solve real-life problems.	1 2 3 4	
9.3 Similar Right Triangles		
Learning Target: Use proportional relationships in right triangles.	1 2 3 4	
I can explain the Right Triangle Similarity Theorem.	1 2 3 4	
I can find the geometric mean of two numbers.	1 2 3 4	
I can find missing dimensions in right triangles.	1 2 3 4	

Chapter Self-Assessment (continued)

	Rating	Date
9.4 The Tangent Ratio		
Learning Target: Understand and use the tangent ratio.	1 2 3 4	
I can explain the tangent ratio.	1 2 3 4	
I can find tangent ratios.	1 2 3 4	
I can use tangent ratios to solve real-life problems.	1 2 3 4	
9.5 The Sine and Cosine Ratios		
Learning Target: Understand and use the sine and cosine ratios.	1 2 3 4	
I can explain the sine and cosine ratios.	1 2 3 4	
I can find sine and cosine ratios.	1 2 3 4	
I can use sine and cosine ratios to solve real-life problems.	1 2 3 4	
H 9.6 Law of Sines and Law of Cosines		
Learning Target: Find unknown side lengths and angle measures of acute and obtuse triangles.	1 2 3 4	
I can find areas of triangles using formulas that involve sines.	1 2 3 4	
I can use inverse trigonometric ratios to approximate angle measures.	1 2 3 4	
I can find unknown measures in triangles using the Law of Sines.	1 2 3 4	
I can find unknown measures in triangles using the Law of Cosines.	1 2 3 4	

Chapter 9

B.E.S.T. Test Prep

1. Which of the following is an approximation of $m\angle C$?

  Ⓐ 35.8°

  Ⓑ 43.8°

  Ⓒ 46.2°

  Ⓓ 54.2°

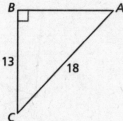

2. What is the perimeter of the parallelogram?

  Ⓐ 26 units

  Ⓑ 38 units

  Ⓒ 52 units

  Ⓓ 74 units

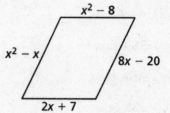

3. Which of the following are possible measures of $\angle WXZ$?

  Ⓐ 39°

  Ⓑ 51°

  Ⓒ 63°

  Ⓓ 68°

  Ⓔ 82°

4. Which proportions are true? Select all that apply.

  Ⓐ $\dfrac{AD}{AC} = \dfrac{AC}{AB}$

  Ⓑ $\dfrac{AD}{AC} = \dfrac{CD}{CB}$

  Ⓒ $\dfrac{AB}{CB} = \dfrac{BD}{DC}$

  Ⓓ $\dfrac{DC}{AC} = \dfrac{CB}{AB}$

  Ⓔ $\dfrac{AC}{AB} = \dfrac{DC}{AC}$

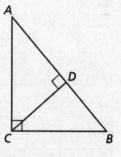

5. Which angle pair is illustrated by $\angle 5$ and $\angle 11$?

  Ⓐ corresponding angles

  Ⓑ alternate interior angles

  Ⓒ alternate exterior angles

  Ⓓ consecutive interior angles

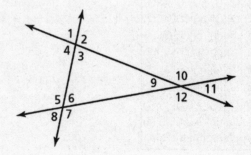

6. Which of the following segment lengths form an acute triangle?

  Ⓐ 9, 12, 15   Ⓒ 7, 10, 12

  Ⓑ 3, 6, 7   Ⓓ 11, 14, 18

Chapter 9

B.E.S.T. Test Prep (continued)

7. For which of the following cases should you use the Law of Cosines?

   Ⓐ AAS case

   Ⓑ SSA case

   Ⓒ ASA case

   Ⓓ SSS case

8. $m\angle XYZ = 110°$, $m\angle XYW = (9x + 6)°$, and $m\angle WYZ = (40 - x)°$. What is $m\angle XYW$?

   Ⓐ 32°

   Ⓑ 55°

   Ⓒ 55.5°

   Ⓓ 78°

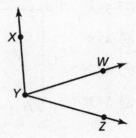

9. What is the value of x? Round to the nearest thousandth.

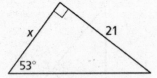

10. What is the area, in square units, of the triangle? Round to the nearest hundredth.

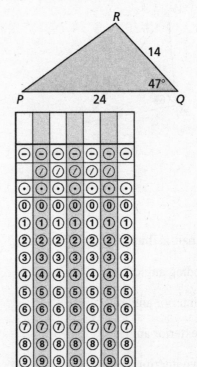

11. Complete the similarity statement.

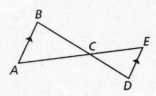

   $\triangle ABC \sim$ _____

12. Point D is the centroid of $\triangle ABC$, $DC = 8x - 6$, and $ED = 3x + 2$. What is CE?

   Ⓐ 10

   Ⓑ 15

   Ⓒ 34

   Ⓓ 51

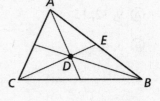

Chapter 9

B.E.S.T. Test Prep (continued)

13. Which of the following can be concluded from the diagram?

  Ⓐ $k \parallel \ell$

  Ⓑ $\angle DCB$ and $\angle BCE$ form a linear pair.

  Ⓒ Point C is the midpoint of $\overline{DE}$.

  Ⓓ $\overrightarrow{BC} \perp \overrightarrow{DC}$

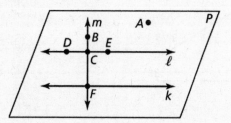

14. Which of the following transformations maps $\triangle ABC$ to $\triangle XYZ$?

  Ⓐ reflection in the line $x = 4$

  Ⓑ 270° rotation about the origin

  Ⓒ translation 4 units right

  Ⓓ reflection in the y-axis

15. What is the value of y?

  Ⓐ −3

  Ⓑ 4

  Ⓒ 5

  Ⓓ 7

16. $\triangle FGH \sim \triangle QRS$. Which statement is false?

  Ⓐ $m\angle G = m\angle R$

  Ⓑ $\dfrac{FG}{GH} = \dfrac{QR}{RS}$

  Ⓒ $\dfrac{FH}{QS} = \dfrac{GH}{RS}$

  Ⓓ $\dfrac{GH}{RS} = \dfrac{QR}{FG}$

17. Write sin 76° in terms of cosine.

_____

18. What is tan B?

  Ⓐ $\dfrac{3}{2}$

  Ⓑ $\dfrac{\sqrt{13}}{2}$

  Ⓒ $\dfrac{3\sqrt{13}}{13}$

  Ⓓ $\dfrac{\sqrt{13}}{3}$

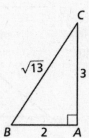

19. What is the geometric mean of 20 and 45?

  Ⓐ $\sqrt{65}$

  Ⓑ 25

  Ⓒ 30

  Ⓓ 32.5

Chapter 9

B.E.S.T. Test Prep (continued)

20. What is the value of x?

Ⓐ $\sqrt{3}$

Ⓑ $\sqrt{6}$

Ⓒ 3

Ⓓ 6

$2\sqrt{3}$

30°

x

21. What is the area of the triangle?

Ⓐ 30 m²

Ⓑ 60 m²

Ⓒ 65 m²

Ⓓ 130 m²

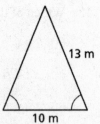

13 m

10 m

22. You fly a kite using a 7-meter string. The angle of elevation from your hands to the kite is 54°. Your hands are 1.5 meters above the ground. How far above the ground, in meters, is the kite? Round to the nearest hundredth of a meter.

23. Using the tick marks and arcs shown in the five triangles, which triangles are congruent to △ABC? Select all that apply.

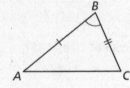

Ⓐ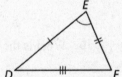

Ⓒ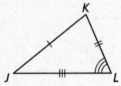

Ⓑ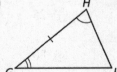

Ⓓ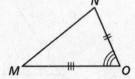

10.1 Review & Refresh

In Exercises 1 and 2, solve the triangle.

1.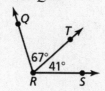

2.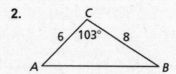

In Exercises 3 and 4, find the indicated measure.

3. $m\angle QRS$

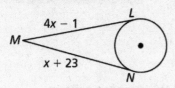

4. YZ

$$\begin{array}{c} \overset{\longleftarrow 32 \longrightarrow}{\underset{19}{}} \\ \overset{\bullet}{X} \quad \overset{\bullet}{Y} \quad \overset{\bullet}{Z} \end{array}$$

5. Tell whether the lines through the given points are *parallel*, *perpendicular*, or *neither*.

   Line 1: $(4, 7), (0, 2)$

   Line 2: $(-3, -6), (1, -1)$

6. Point L and N are points of tangency. Find the value of x.

7. Find the vertical distance covered by the slide.

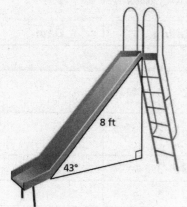

Name _____ Date _____

8. Point P is the centroid of $\triangle ABC$. Find AP and DP when $AD = 42$.

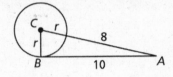

9. Point B is a point of tangency. Find the radius r of $\odot C$.

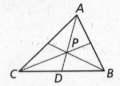

10. Points B and D are points of tangency. Find the value(s) of x.

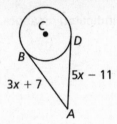

11. Two sidewalks are tangent to a circular park centered at P, as shown.

   a. What is the length of sidewalk $\overline{AB}$? Explain.

   b. What is the diameter of the park?

Use the scale to rate your understanding of the learning target and the success criteria.

| 1 | I do not understand yet. | 2 | I can do it with help. | 3 | I can do it on my own. | 4 | I can teach someone else. |

	Rating	Date
10.1 Lines and Segments That Intersect Circles		
Learning Target: Identify lines and segments that intersect circles and use them to solve problems.	1 2 3 4	
I can identify special segments and lines that intersect circles.	1 2 3 4	
I can draw and identify common tangents.	1 2 3 4	
I can use properties of tangents to solve problems.	1 2 3 4	

10.2 Review & Refresh

1. Points B and D are points of tangency. Find the value(s) of x.

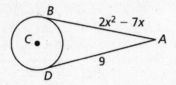

2. Name the minor arc and find its measure. Then name the major arc and find its measure.

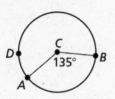

3. Find YZ.

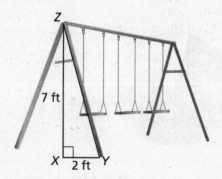

4. Find the geometric mean of 16 and 45.

In Exercises 5 and 6, find the value of x.

5.

6.

95°
85°
$x°$
150°
90°

Name _____ Date _____

7. Graph $\triangle ABC$ with vertices $A(3, 1)$, $B(-1, 2)$, and $C(0, -2)$ and its image after a 180° rotation about the origin.

8. Find $m\angle ABC$. Explain your reasoning.

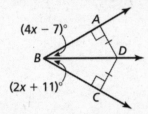

$(4x - 7)°$

$(2x + 11)°$

In Exercises 9–11, a recent survey asked high school students to name their favorite movie genre. The results are shown in the circle graph. Find the indicated arc measure.

9. $m\widehat{AF}$

10. $m\widehat{GDC}$

11. $m\widehat{DFC}$

Favorite Movie Genre

Science Fiction: 6%
Other: 4%
Horror: 12%
Action: 20%
Fantasy: 10%
Adventure: 15%
Drama: 8%
Comedy: 25%

Use the scale to rate your understanding of the learning target and the success criteria.

| 1 | I do not understand yet. | 2 | I can do it with help. | 3 | I can do it on my own. | 4 | I can teach someone else. |

	Rating	Date
10.2 Finding Arc Measures		
Learning Target: Understand arc measures and similar circles.	1 2 3 4	
I can find arc measures.	1 2 3 4	
I can identify congruent arcs.	1 2 3 4	
I can prove that all circles are similar. **H**	1 2 3 4	

10.3 Review & Refresh

1. Point *B* is a point of tangency. Find the radius *x* of ⊙*Q*.

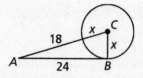

In Exercises 2 and 3, find the missing interior angle measure.

2. Quadrilateral *WXYZ* has angle measures *m*∠*W* = 66°, *m*∠*X* = 85°, and *m*∠*Z* = 113°. Find *m*∠*Y*.

3. Pentagon *ABCDE* has angle measures *m*∠*B* = 90°, *m*∠*C* = 125°, *m*∠*D* = 76°, and *m*∠*E* = 104°. Find *m*∠*A*.

4. Tell whether $\overset{\frown}{MN}$ and $\overset{\frown}{ST}$ are congruent, similar, or neither. Explain.

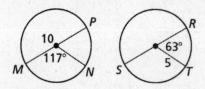

5. A surveyor makes the measurements shown to determine the length of a bridge to be built across a small lake from the West Cabins to the East Cabins. Find the length of the bridge.

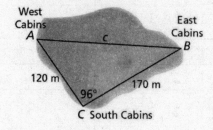

10.3 Review & Refresh (continued)

6. Find $m\overset{\frown}{EH}$ in $\odot Q$.

 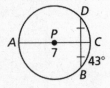 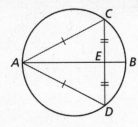

7. Determine whether $\overline{AB}$ is a diameter of the circle. Explain your reasoning.

8. Find the radius of the circle.

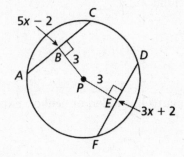

10.3 Self-Assessment

Use the scale to rate your understanding of the learning target and the success criteria.

| **1** I do not understand yet. | **2** I can do it with help. | **3** I can do it on my own. | **4** I can teach someone else. |

	Rating	Date
10.3 Using Chords		
Learning Target: Understand and apply theorems about chords.	1 2 3 4	
I can use chords of circles to find arc measures.	1 2 3 4	
I can use chords of circles to find lengths.	1 2 3 4	
I can describe the relationship between a diameter and a chord perpendicular to a diameter.	1 2 3 4	
I can find the center of a circle given three points on the circle.	1 2 3 4	

10.4 Review & Refresh

1. Describe a congruence transformation that maps △*ABC* to △*DEF*.

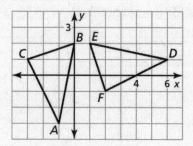

2. Find the radius of ⊙*A*.

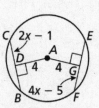

In Exercises 3–5, identify the given arc as a *major arc*, *minor arc*, or *semicircle*. Then find the measure of the arc.

3. $\overparen{YZ}$

4. $\overparen{XYZ}$

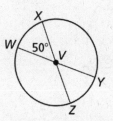

5. $\overparen{WZX}$

6. Tell whether $\overline{AB}$ is tangent to ⊙*C*. Explain your reasoning.

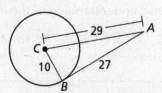

In Exercises 7 and 8, find the indicated measure.

7. $m\angle QRS$

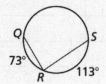

8. $m\angle DFE$

10.4 Review & Refresh (continued)

9. You and your friend leave school heading in opposite directions. You each travel 0.7 mile, then change directions and travel 0.5 mile. You start due west and then turn 30° toward south. Your friend starts due east and then turns 15° toward north. Who is farther from the school? Explain your reasoning.

10. Name two pairs of congruent angles.

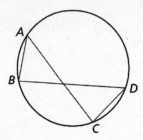

In Exercises 11 and 12, find the value of each variable.

11.

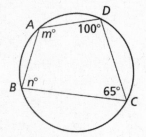

12.

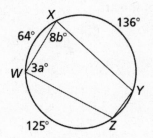

10.4 Self-Assessment

Use the scale to rate your understanding of the learning target and the success criteria.

1 I do not understand yet.	2 I can do it with help.	3 I can do it on my own.	4 I can teach someone else.

	Rating	Date
10.4 Inscribed Angles and Polygons		
Learning Target: Use properties of inscribed angles and inscribed polygons.	1 2 3 4	
I can find measures of inscribed angles and intercepted arcs.	1 2 3 4	
I can find angle measures of inscribed polygons.	1 2 3 4	
I can construct a square inscribed in a circle. **H**	1 2 3 4	

10.5 Review & Refresh

1. Find the perimeter and area of the triangle with vertices $A(5, -6)$, $B(-3, -6)$, and $C(5, 7)$.

2. A diver is using sonar to track a shark that is circling his submarine. $m\angle BSC = 127°$. Find $m\overarc{AC}$. Explain your reasoning.

In Exercises 3 and 4, find the value of x.

3.
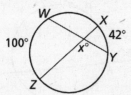
100°   42° $x°$

4.
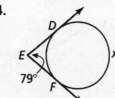
79° $x°$

In Exercises 5 and 6, find the indicated measure.

5. $m\angle K$

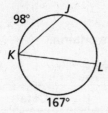
98°   167°

6. $m\overarc{ST}$

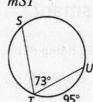
73°   95°

7. Graph $\triangle PQR$ with vertices $P\left(1, \frac{1}{2}\right)$, $Q\left(-\frac{3}{2}, 1\right)$, and $R\left(\frac{1}{2}, \frac{3}{2}\right)$ and its image after a dilation with a scale factor of 4.

10.5   Review & Refresh (continued)

In Exercises 8–10, line *t* is tangent to the circle. Find the indicated measure.

8. $m\overarc{AB}$

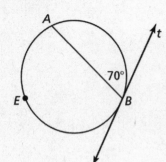

9. $m\overarc{XY}$

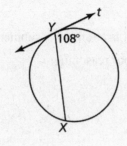

10. $m\angle 2$

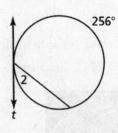

In Exercises 11–13, find the value of *x*.

11.

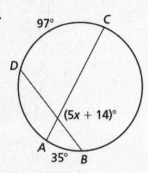

12.

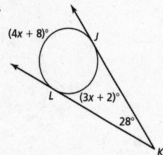

13.

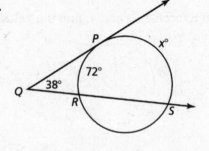

10.5   Self-Assessment

Use the scale to rate your understanding of the learning target and the success criteria.

| 1 | I do not understand yet. | 2 | I can do it with help. | 3 | I can do it on my own. | 4 | I can teach someone else. |

	Rating	Date
10.5 Angle Relationships in Circles		
Learning Target: Understand angles formed by chords, secants, and tangents.	1 2 3 4	
I can identify angles and arcs determined by chords, secants, and tangents.	1 2 3 4	
I can find angle measures and arc measures involving chords, secants, and tangents.	1 2 3 4	
I can use circumscribed angles to solve problems.	1 2 3 4	

Name_____ Date_____

10.6 Review & Refresh

1. Find the radius of ⊙*A*.

2. You measure your distance from a column and the angle of elevation from the ground to the top of the column. Find the height of the column.

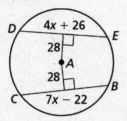

In Exercises 3–5, find the indicated measure.

3. *WY*

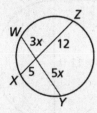

4. $m\widehat{RS}$

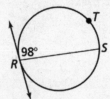

5. $m\widehat{UV}$

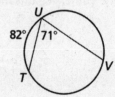

6. Show that △*EGH* and △*EFG* are similar.

10.6 Review & Refresh (continued)

7. Find the value of *x* that makes *m* ‖ *n*. Explain your reasoning.

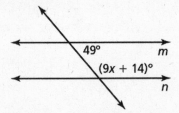

8. You go swimming in a circular pool. Your sandals are 9 feet from the ladder of the pool. The distance from the sandals to the pool is 5 feet. What is the diameter of the pool?

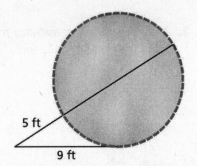

9. The Xs in the diagram show the positions of two basketball teammates relative to the free throw circle on a basketball court. The player outside the circle passes the ball to the player on the circle. What is the length of the pass?

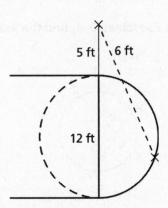

10.6 Self-Assessment

Use the scale to rate your understanding of the learning target and the success criteria.

| 1 | I do not understand yet. | 2 | I can do it with help. | 3 | I can do it on my own. | 4 | I can teach someone else. |

	Rating	Date
10.6 Segment Relationships in Circles		
Learning Target: Use theorems about segments of chords, secants, and tangents.	1 2 3 4	
I can find lengths of segments of chords.	1 2 3 4	
I can identify segments of secants and tangents.	1 2 3 4	
I can find lengths of segments of secants and tangents.	1 2 3 4	

10.7 Review & Refresh

1. Write the standard equation of the circle with center $(-3, 5)$ that passes through the point $(-8, -7)$.

In Exercises 2 and 3, find the value of x.

2.

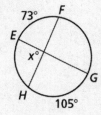

3.

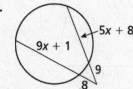

In Exercises 4–7, identify the arc as a *major arc*, *minor arc*, or *semicircle*. Then find the measure of the arc.

4. $\overgroup{BDE}$

5. $\overgroup{AC}$

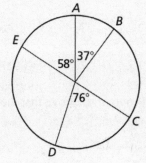

6. $\overgroup{ADC}$

7. $\overgroup{CDE}$

8. Find $m\angle Y$.

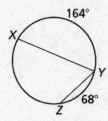

9. The lines painted for the parking spaces are parallel. Find $m\angle 2$.

10.7 Review & Refresh (continued)

10. Find the value of x that makes $\triangle DEF \sim \triangle GHI$.

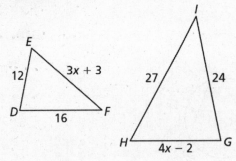

11. Find the center and radius of the circle. Then graph the circle.

$$x^2 + y^2 + 2x + 2y = 2$$

12. Prove or disprove that the point $(-1, 2)$ lies on the circle centered at $(-4, -1)$ with radius $3\sqrt{2}$.

10.7 Self-Assessment

Use the scale to rate your understanding of the learning target and the success criteria.

| 1 | I do not understand yet. | 2 | I can do it with help. | 3 | I can do it on my own. | 4 | I can teach someone else. |

	Rating	Date
10.7 Circles in the Coordinate Plane		
Learning Target: Understand equations of circles.	1　2　3　4	
I can write equations of circles.	1　2　3　4	
I can find the center and radius of a circle.	1　2　3　4	
I can graph equations of circles.	1　2　3　4	
I can write coordinate proofs involving circles.	1　2　3　4	

Name_____ Date _____

Chapter 10

Chapter Self-Assessment

Use the scale to rate your understanding of the learning target and the success criteria.

| 1 | I do not understand yet. | 2 | I can do it with help. | 3 | I can do it on my own. | 4 | I can teach someone else. |

	Rating	Date
Chapter 10 Circles		
Learning Target: Understand and apply circle relationships.	1 2 3 4	
I can identify lines and segments that intersect circles.	1 2 3 4	
I can find angle and arc measures in circles.	1 2 3 4	
I can use circle relationships to solve problems.	1 2 3 4	
I can use circles to model and solve real-life problems.	1 2 3 4	
10.1 Lines and Segments That Intersect Circles		
Learning Target: Identify lines and segments that intersect circles and use them to solve problems.	1 2 3 4	
I can identify special segments and lines that intersect circles.	1 2 3 4	
I can draw and identify common tangents.	1 2 3 4	
I can use properties of tangents to solve problems.	1 2 3 4	
10.2 Finding Arc Measures		
Learning Target: Understand arc measures and similar circles.	1 2 3 4	
I can find arc measures.	1 2 3 4	
I can identify congruent arcs.	1 2 3 4	
I can prove that all circles are similar. **H**	1 2 3 4	
10.3 Using Chords		
Learning Target: Understand and apply theorems about chords.	1 2 3 4	
I can use chords of circles to find arc measures.	1 2 3 4	
I can use chords of circles to find lengths.	1 2 3 4	
I can describe the relationship between a diameter and a chord perpendicular to a diameter.	1 2 3 4	
I can find the center of a circle given three points on the circle.	1 2 3 4	
10.4 Inscribed Angles and Polygons		
Learning Target: Use properties of inscribed angles and inscribed polygons.	1 2 3 4	
I can find measures of inscribed angles and intercepted arcs.	1 2 3 4	
I can find angle measures of inscribed polygons.	1 2 3 4	
I can construct a square inscribed in a circle. **H**	1 2 3 4	

Chapter 10 Chapter Self-Assessment (continued)

	Rating	Date
10.5 Angle Relationships in Circles		
Learning Target: Understand angles formed by chords, secants, and tangents.	1 2 3 4	
I can identify angles and arcs determined by chords, secants, and tangents.	1 2 3 4	
I can find angle measures and arc measures involving chords, secants, and tangents.	1 2 3 4	
I can use circumscribed angles to solve problems.	1 2 3 4	
10.6 Segment Relationships in Circles		
Learning Target: Use theorems about segments of chords, secants, and tangents.	1 2 3 4	
I can find lengths of segments of chords.	1 2 3 4	
I can identify segments of secants and tangents.	1 2 3 4	
I can find lengths of segments of secants and tangents.	1 2 3 4	
10.7 Circles in the Coordinate Plane		
Learning Target: Understand equations of circles.	1 2 3 4	
I can write equations of circles.	1 2 3 4	
I can find the center and radius of a circle.	1 2 3 4	
I can graph equations of circles.	1 2 3 4	
I can write coordinate proofs involving circles.	1 2 3 4	

Chapter 10

B.E.S.T. Test Prep

1. Segments that are tangent to the circle form a quadrilateral. What is the perimeter of the quadrilateral?

   Ⓐ 15 m

   Ⓑ 21 m

   Ⓒ 26 m

   Ⓓ 30 m

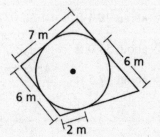

2. The measure of one interior angle of a parallelogram is 30° more than 5 times the measure of another interior angle. What is the measure of the smaller angle?

   Ⓐ 25°

   Ⓑ 30°

   Ⓒ 36°

   Ⓓ 55°

3. Write the standard equation of the circle with center $(-5, 12)$ that passes through the point $(-9, 15)$.

   _____

4. Which arc is a major arc?

   Ⓐ $\overarc{BE}$

   Ⓑ $\overarc{ADC}$

   Ⓒ $\overarc{CBA}$

   Ⓓ $\overarc{BDA}$

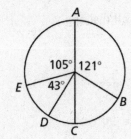

5. What is the area of the isosceles trapezoid?

   Ⓐ about 45.0 cm²

   Ⓑ about 63.2 cm²

   Ⓒ about 83.9 cm²

   Ⓓ about 94.0 cm²

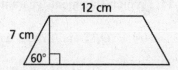

6. Which congruence statements are true? Select all that apply.

   Ⓐ $\overline{KN} \cong \overline{JN}$

   Ⓑ $\angle JLM \cong \angle MKJ$

   Ⓒ $\overline{MN} \cong \overline{LN}$

   Ⓓ $\overline{KM} \cong \overline{LJ}$

   Ⓔ $\triangle LMN \cong \triangle LKJ$

   Ⓕ $\triangle KLM \cong \triangle LKJ$

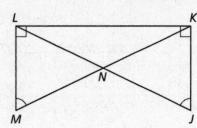

7. What is the radius of ⊙*E*?

Ⓐ 21

Ⓑ 29

Ⓒ 42

Ⓓ 46.5

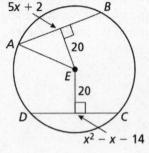

8. What is the perimeter of △*ABC*?

Ⓐ about 24.8 ft

Ⓑ about 28.4 ft

Ⓒ about 34.0 ft

Ⓓ about 37.5 ft

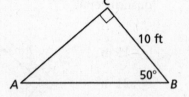

9. $\overline{BE}$ is a midsegment of △*ACD*. What is the perimeter of trapezoid *BCDE*?

Ⓐ 14 m

Ⓑ 20 m

Ⓒ 28 m

Ⓓ 31 m

10. In trapezoid *ABCD*, $\overline{AB} \parallel \overline{CD}$, *CD* = 4 • *AB*, and $\overline{MN}$ is the midsegment of *ABCD*. What is the ratio of *CD* to *MN*?

Ⓐ 2 : 5

Ⓑ 5 : 8

Ⓒ 8 : 5

Ⓓ 5 : 2

11. Which statements guarantee that △*QRS* ~ △*XYZ*? Select all that apply.

Ⓐ △*QRS* and △*XYZ* are equilateral.

Ⓑ *m∠Q* = 39°, *m∠R* = 56°, *m∠X* = 39°, and *m∠Z* = 95°.

Ⓒ △*XYZ* is a right isosceles triangle and *m∠Q* + *m∠R* = 90°.

Ⓓ *m∠R* = 107°, *m∠S* = 25°, *m∠X* = 48°, and *m∠Y* = 107°.

Ⓔ *m∠Q* + *m∠S* = 138° and *m∠Y* + *m∠Z* = 116°.

12. What is the value of *x*?

Ⓐ 42

Ⓑ 48

Ⓒ 84

Ⓓ 96

13. What is *m∠QUT*?

Ⓐ 42°

Ⓑ 54.3°

Ⓒ 85.2°

Ⓓ 138°

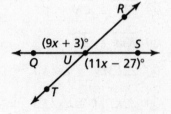

Chapter 10

B.E.S.T. Test Prep (continued)

14. What is the difference of the geometric mean and the arithmetic mean of 18 and 128?

15. What is the value of x rounded to the nearest thousandth?

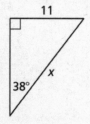

16. What is the value of y?

Ⓐ 21

Ⓑ 23

Ⓒ 42

Ⓓ 46

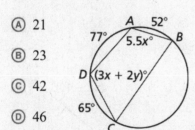

17. What is $m\overarc{QS}$?

Ⓐ 25

Ⓑ 32

Ⓒ 43

Ⓓ 52

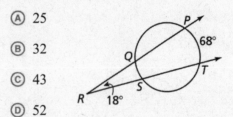

18. Point B is a point of tangency. What is the radius r of $\odot C$?

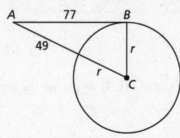

Chapter 10 ° **B.E.S.T. Test Prep** (continued)

19. What is *AB*?

Ⓐ 2

Ⓑ 5

Ⓒ 8

Ⓓ 16

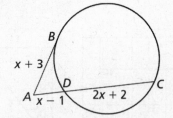

20. What is the radius of the circle?

Ⓐ 10.4

Ⓑ 14.3

Ⓒ 20.8

Ⓓ 28.6

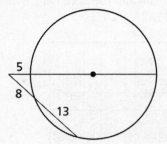

21. You graph the circle $(x + 3)^2 + (y - 2)^2 = 25$ and the line $x = -8$ in a coordinate plane. Which statement is true?

Ⓐ The line is a tangent of the circle.

Ⓑ The line is a secant of the circle.

Ⓒ The line is a secant that contains the diameter of the circle.

Ⓓ The line does not pass through the circle.

22. What is $m\angle R$?

Ⓐ 24°

Ⓑ 28°

Ⓒ 48°

Ⓓ 96°

23. What is $m\angle A$?

Ⓐ 12.25°

Ⓑ 23.5°

Ⓒ 38.75°

Ⓓ 51.25°

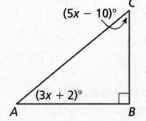

24. $\triangle XYZ$ has vertices $X(-2, 1)$, $Y(3, -1)$, and $Z(1, 4)$. What are the vertices of its image after a dilation with a scale factor of 4?

_____

11.1 Review & Refresh

In Exercises 1 and 2, find the area of the polygon with the given vertices.

1. $A(-4, 7), B(8, 7), C(-4, 2)$

2. $W(3, 8), X(3, -1), Y(-5, -1), Z(-5, 8)$

3. Find the length of the midsegment of the trapezoid.

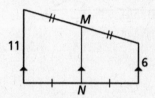

In Exercises 4 and 5, find the center and radius of the circle. Then graph the circle.

4. $x^2 + y^2 = 9$

5. $x^2 + y^2 - 8x = 20$

11.1 Review & Refresh (continued)

In Exercises 6–8, find the value of x.

6.

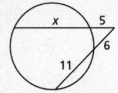

7.

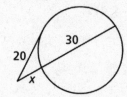

8.

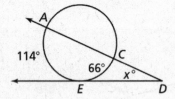

11.1 Self-Assessment

Use the scale to rate your understanding of the learning target and the success criteria.

| **1** I do not understand yet. | **2** I can do it with help. | **3** I can do it on my own. | **4** I can teach someone else. |

	Rating	Date
11.1 Circumference and Arc Length		
Learning Target: Understand circumference, arc length, and radian measure.	1 2 3 4	
I can use the formula for the circumference of a circle to find measures.	1 2 3 4	
I can find arc lengths and use arc lengths to find measures.	1 2 3 4	
I can solve real-life problems involving circumference.	1 2 3 4	
I can explain radian measure and convert between degree and radian measure.	1 2 3 4	

11.2 Review & Refresh

1. Find the area of the shaded region.

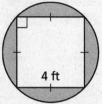

4 ft

In Exercises 2 and 3, find the indicated measure.

2. $m\overset{\frown}{AB}$

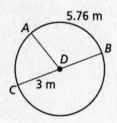

5.76 m

A

D

B

C

3 m

3. $m\angle MQN$

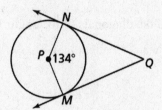

N

P • 134°

Q

M

4. Graph $x = \frac{1}{16}(y - 3)^2 + 2$. Identify the focus, directrix, and axis of symmetry.

5. Find the distance from the point $(-1, -2)$ to the line $y = \frac{1}{2}x + 6$.

6. Point D is the centroid of $\triangle ABC$. Find DE and BE when $BD = 18$.

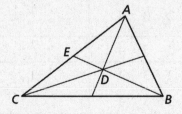

A

E

D

C

B

11.2 Review & Refresh (continued)

7. A *pediment* is the upper triangular part of a façade of classical architecture. Prove that the lengths of both sides of the pediment are the same.

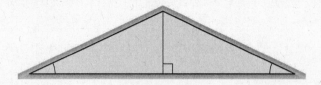

8. Find the lengths of the diagonals of rectangle $WXYZ$ when $WY = 6x - 1$ and $XZ = 8x - 7$.

9. The endpoints of $\overline{MN}$ are $M(-6, 1)$ and $N(-2, 9)$. Write an equation of the perpendicular bisector of $\overline{MN}$.

11.2 Self-Assessment

Use the scale to rate your understanding of the learning target and the success criteria.

| 1 | I do not understand yet. | 2 | I can do it with help. | 3 | I can do it on my own. | 4 | I can teach someone else. |

	Rating	Date
11.2 Areas of Circles and Sectors		
Learning Target: Find areas of circles and areas of sectors of circles.	1 2 3 4	
I can use the formula for area of a circle to find measures.	1 2 3 4	
I can find areas of sectors of circles.	1 2 3 4	
I can solve problems involving areas of sectors.	1 2 3 4	

Name_____ Date_____

11.3 Review & Refresh

In Exercises 1 and 2, find the indicated measure.

1. area of ⊙F

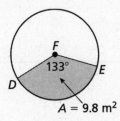

$A = 9.8 \text{ m}^2$

2. arc length of $\overarc{JK}$

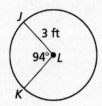

3. Graph the circle $x^2 + y^2 + 8x - 4y = 5$. Identify the domain and range.

4. △ABC has vertices $A(-1, 3)$, $B(-1, -1)$, and $C(0, 1)$. △DEF has vertices $D(0, 5)$, $E(0, -3)$, and $F(2, 1)$. Are the triangles similar? Use transformations to explain your reasoning.

In Exercises 5 and 6, find the value of x.

5.

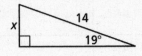

6.

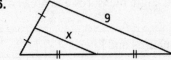

11.3 Review & Refresh (continued)

7. Find the area of the regular hexagon.

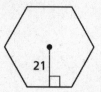

8. An eraser is shown.

    a. State which theorem you can use to show that the side of the eraser is in the shape of a parallelogram.

    b. Find $m\angle A$, $m\angle C$, and $m\angle D$.

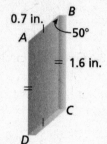

9. Find the measure of the exterior angle.

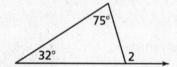

11.3 Self-Assessment

Use the scale to rate your understanding of the learning target and the success criteria.

| **1** I do not understand yet. | **2** I can do it with help. | **3** I can do it on my own. | **4** I can teach someone else. |

	Rating	Date
11.3 Areas of Polygons		
Learning Target: Find angle measures and areas of regular polygons.	1 2 3 4	
I can find areas of rhombuses and kites.	1 2 3 4	
I can find angle measures in regular polygons.	1 2 3 4	
I can find areas of regular polygons.	1 2 3 4	
I can explain how the area of a triangle is related to the area formulas for rhombuses, kites, and regular polygons.	1 2 3 4	

Name_____ Date_____

In Exercises 1 and 2, find the indicated measure.

1. $m\overarc{WXY}$

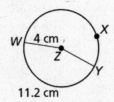

2. area of each sector

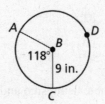

3. In the diagram, *ABCDEFG* is a regular heptagon inscribed in $\odot H$. The radius of the circle is 5 units. Find the area of the heptagon.

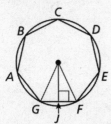

4. About 545,000 people live in a circular region with a population density of about 1175 people per square mile. Find the radius of the region.

5. A school swimming pool is being remodeled. The pool will be similar to an Olympic-size pool, which has a length of 50 meters and a width of 25 meters. The school plans to make the length of the new pool 40 meters. Find the perimeters of an Olympic-size pool and the new pool.

11.4 Review & Refresh (continued)

6. How does *JL* compare to *SQ*? Explain your reasoning.

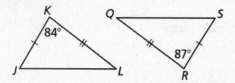

7. Find the value of each variable using sine and cosine.

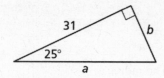

8. Find the sum of the measures of the interior angles of a 23-gon.

9. Find the geometric mean of 32 and 50.

11.4 Self-Assessment

Use the scale to rate your understanding of the learning target and the success criteria.

| **1** I do not understand yet. | **2** I can do it with help. | **3** I can do it on my own. | **4** I can teach someone else. |

	Rating	Date
11.4 Modeling with Area		
Learning Target: Understand the concept of population density and modeling with area.	1 2 3 4	
I can explain what population density means.	1 2 3 4	
I can find and use population densities.	1 2 3 4	
I can use area formulas to solve problems.	1 2 3 4	

Name_____ Date _____

Use the scale to rate your understanding of the learning target and the success criteria.

| **1** I do not understand yet. | **2** I can do it with help. | **3** I can do it on my own. | **4** I can teach someone else. |

	Rating	Date
Chapter 11 Circumference and Area		
Learning Target: Understand circumference and area.	1 2 3 4	
I can find circumferences of circles and arc lengths of sectors.	1 2 3 4	
I can find areas of circles and sectors.	1 2 3 4	
I can find areas of polygons.	1 2 3 4	
I can solve real-life problems involving area.	1 2 3 4	
11.1 Circumference and Arc Length		
Learning Target: Understand circumference, arc length, and radian measure.	1 2 3 4	
I can use the formula for the circumference of a circle to find measures.	1 2 3 4	
I can find arc lengths and use arc lengths to find measures.	1 2 3 4	
I can solve real-life problems involving circumference.	1 2 3 4	
I can explain radian measure and convert between degree and radian measure.	1 2 3 4	
11.2 Areas of Circles and Sectors		
Learning Target: Find areas of circles and areas of sectors of circles.	1 2 3 4	
I can use the formula for area of a circle to find measures.	1 2 3 4	
I can find areas of sectors of circles.	1 2 3 4	
I can solve problems involving areas of sectors.	1 2 3 4	
11.3 Areas of Polygons		
Learning Target: Find angle measures and areas of regular polygons.	1 2 3 4	
I can find areas of rhombuses and kites.	1 2 3 4	
I can find angle measures in regular polygons.	1 2 3 4	
I can find areas of regular polygons.	1 2 3 4	
I can explain how the area of a triangle is related to the area formulas for rhombuses, kites, and regular polygons.	1 2 3 4	

Chapter 11 Chapter Self-Assessment (continued)

	Rating	Date
11.4 Modeling with Area		
Learning Target: Understand the concept of population density and modeling with area.	1 2 3 4	
I can explain what population density means.	1 2 3 4	
I can find and use population densities.	1 2 3 4	
I can use area formulas to solve problems.	1 2 3 4	

Chapter 11 B.E.S.T. Test Prep

1. About 1.28 million people live in a circular region with an 18-mile radius. What is the population density in people per square mile?

   (A) 1258

   (B) 3951

   (C) 5361

   (D) 10,722

2. A 60° arc in ⊙A and a 24° arc in ⊙B have the same length. What is the ratio of the radius of ⊙A to the radius of ⊙B?

   (A) 1 to 15

   (B) 1 to 6

   (C) 2 to 5

   (D) 5 to 2

3. Point M lies on $\overline{AB}$, AB = 24, and BM = 13. What is AM?

   (A) 11

   (B) 12

   (C) 24

   (D) 37

4. What is the area of a regular nonagon with an apothem of 4 units?

   (A) about 23.1 square units

   (B) about 26.2 square units

   (C) about 46.3 square units

   (D) about 52.4 square units

5. What is the value of x that makes m ∥ n?

   (A) $1\frac{1}{3}$

   (B) 8

   (C) 20

   (D) 40

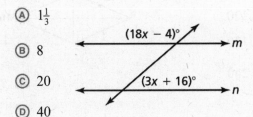

6. What is $m\overarc{AC}$?

   (A) 113°

   (B) 137°

   (C) 156°

   (D) 223°

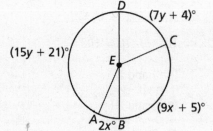

7. ⊙X ≅ ⊙Y. Which of the following statements are true? Select all that apply.

   (A) GH = 10

   (B) AE = 5

   (C) $m\overarc{AD}$ = 106°

   (D) $m\overarc{FH}$ = 148°

   (E) m∠FHG = 74°

   (F) GY = 6.3

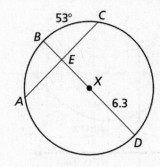

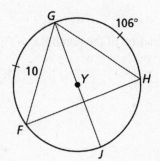

Chapter 11 **B.E.S.T. Test Prep** (continued)

8. Which graph represents the equation $x^2 + y^2 - 6x + 2y = 6$?

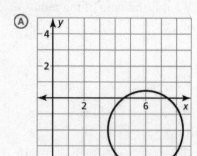

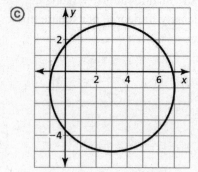

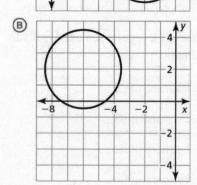

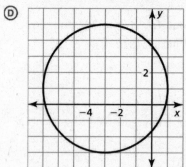

9. Which statements contradict each other?

  I. $\triangle ABC$ is a right triangle.

  II. $m\angle A = 41°$

  III. $m\angle B = 103°$

  Ⓐ I and II

  Ⓑ I and III

  Ⓒ II and III

  Ⓓ None of the statements are contradictory.

10. What is the area of the rhombus?

  Ⓐ 65

  Ⓑ 120

  Ⓒ 130

  Ⓓ 240

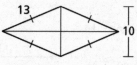

11. Write an equation of the parabola.

  _____

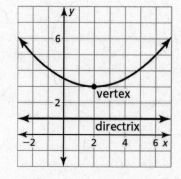

Chapter 11

B.E.S.T. Test Prep (continued)

12. What is the perimeter of the triangle?

Ⓐ $8\sqrt{3}$ cm

Ⓑ $12 + 4\sqrt{3}$ cm

Ⓒ $8 + 8\sqrt{2}$ cm

Ⓓ $24 + 8\sqrt{3}$ cm

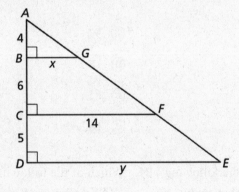

8 cm

30°

13. What is the radius of ⊙C?

Ⓐ 10 in.

Ⓑ 17.7 in.

Ⓒ 36 in.

Ⓓ 63.8 in.

C 100°

A ≈ 1131 in.²

14. What is the area, in square units, of trapezoid *BDEG*?

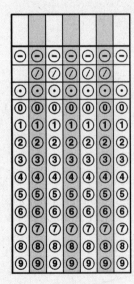

A

4

B ⌐ G

x

6

C ⌐ F

14

5

D ⌐ E

y

15. You have 22.4 yards of fencing to enclose a rectangular garden. What is the maximum area of the garden?

_____

Chapter 11

B.E.S.T. Test Prep (continued)

16. A regular octagon has a perimeter of 41.6 meters. What is the radius rounded to the nearest hundredth of a meter?

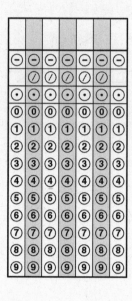

17. What is the area of the shaded region rounded to the nearest hundredth square meter?

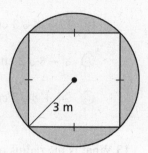

3 m

18. What is the measure of the angle between the x-axis and the line $y = \frac{8}{9}x$?

Ⓐ about 27.3°

Ⓑ about 41.6°

Ⓒ about 48.4°

Ⓓ about 62.7°

19. What is the circumference of the circle $(x - 2)^2 + (y + 5)^2 = 81$?

Ⓐ 9π

Ⓑ 18π

Ⓒ 81π

Ⓓ 162π

20. $\triangle MNP \cong \triangle STU$. Which of the following statements are true? Select all that apply.

Ⓐ $\angle M \cong \angle S$

Ⓑ $\overline{NP} \cong \overline{ST}$

Ⓒ $\triangle PMN \cong \triangle UST$

Ⓓ $\triangle MPN \cong \triangle UTS$

Ⓔ $\overline{MP} \cong \overline{SU}$

21. Which of the following are vertices of the image of $\triangle XYZ$ after a reflection in the y-axis and a dilation with a scale factor of 2? Select all that apply.

Ⓐ $(-8, 4)$

Ⓑ $(2, -4)$

Ⓒ $(-10, 8)$

Ⓓ $(8, 4)$

Ⓔ $(10, 8)$

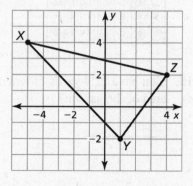

12.1 Review & Refresh

1. Explain how to prove that $\overline{QR} \cong \overline{TS}$.

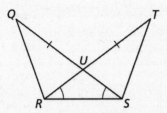

2. Tailors want to know the density of fabric when deciding what material to use when making clothing. The piece shown weighs 3 ounces. Find the density of the fabric in ounces per square yard.

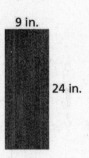

9 in.

24 in.

In Exercises 3 and 4, draw the cross section formed by the described plane that contains the line segment drawn on the solid. What is the shape of the cross section?

3. plane is perpendicular to base

4. plane is parallel to base

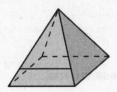

5. Tell whether $\overline{AB}$ is tangent to $\odot C$. Explain your reasoning.

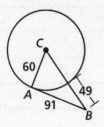

60

49

91

12.1 Review & Refresh (continued)

6. Three vertices of $\square WXYZ$ are $W(-5,1)$, $Y(4,-2)$, and $Z(1,2)$. Find the coordinates of the remaining vertex.

7. Solve the right triangle.

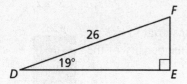

8. Verify that the segment lengths 29, 34, and 51 form a triangle. Is the triangle *acute*, *right*, or *obtuse*?

In Exercises 9 and 10, find the area of the quadrilateral.

9.

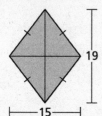

10.

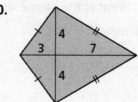

12.1 Self-Assessment

Use the scale to rate your understanding of the learning target and the success criteria.

| 1 | I do not understand yet. | 2 | I can do it with help. | 3 | I can do it on my own. | 4 | I can teach someone else. |

	Rating	Date
12.1 Cross Sections of Solids		
Learning Target: Describe and draw cross sections.	1 2 3 4	
I can describe attributes of solids.	1 2 3 4	
I can describe and draw cross sections.	1 2 3 4	
I can solve real-life problems involving cross sections.	1 2 3 4	

12.2 Review & Refresh

1. In the diagram, $ABCD \cong EFGH$. Find the values of x and y.

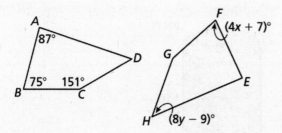

In Exercises 2 and 3, tell whether the solid is a polyhedron. If it is, name the polyhedron.

2.

3.

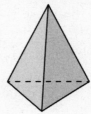

4. In $\triangle PQR$, $m\angle Q = 27°$ and $m\angle R = 79°$. In $\triangle STU$, $m\angle S = 74°$ and $m\angle T = 27°$. Are the triangles similar? Explain.

5. Find the value of x.

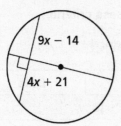

6. An airplane travels 400 miles east, then turns 50° toward north and travels another 550 miles. How far is the airplane from its starting location?

12.2 **Review & Refresh** (continued)

7. Find the surface area of the solid formed by the net.

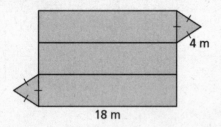

4 m

18 m

8. Find the surface area of the right cylinder.

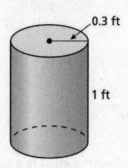

0.3 ft

1 ft

9. Find the area of the regular polygon.

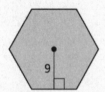

9

12.2 **Self-Assessment**

Use the scale to rate your understanding of the learning target and the success criteria.

| **1** I do not understand yet. | **2** I can do it with help. | **3** I can do it on my own. | **4** I can teach someone else. |

	Rating	Date
12.2 Surface Areas of Prisms and Cylinders		
Learning Target: Find and use surface areas of prisms and cylinders.	1 2 3 4	
I can find surface areas of prisms and cylinders.	1 2 3 4	
I can solve real-life problems involving surface areas of prisms and cylinders.	1 2 3 4	
I can find surface areas of similar prisms and similar cylinders.	1 2 3 4	

12.3   Review & Refresh

In Exercises 1 and 2, find the value of x.

1.

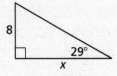

2.

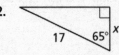

3. Find the area of a regular quadrilateral with side length of 2.5 in.

4. Find the surface area of the right cone.

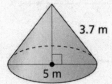

3.7 m

5 m

5. Find the surface area of the regular prism.

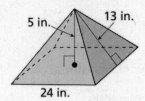

5 in.   13 in.

24 in.

6. Describe the shape formed by the intersection of the plane and the solid.

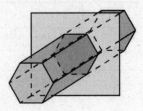

12.3 Review & Refresh (continued)

7. The vertices of $\triangle ABC$ are $A(3, 2)$, $B(6, -1)$, and $C(-1, -3)$. Translate $\triangle ABC$ using the vector $\langle -2, 3 \rangle$. Graph $\triangle ABC$ and its image.

8. The diagram shows the location of a campsite and a trail. You want to choose a campsite that is at least 75 feet from the trail. Does this campsite meet your requirement? Explain.

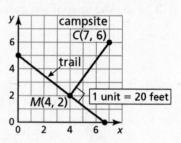

9. Let p be "it is Saturday" and let q be "it is the weekend." Write the conditional statement $p \rightarrow q$ and the contrapositive $\sim q \rightarrow \sim p$ in words. Then decide whether each statement is true or false.

12.3 Self-Assessment

Use the scale to rate your understanding of the learning target and the success criteria.

| 1 | I do not understand yet. | 2 | I can do it with help. | 3 | I can do it on my own. | 4 | I can teach someone else. |

	Rating	Date
12.3 Surface Areas of Pyramids and Cones		
Learning Target: Find and use surface areas of pyramids and cones.	1 2 3 4	
I can find surface areas of pyramids and cones.	1 2 3 4	
I can find surface areas of similar pyramids and similar cones.	1 2 3 4	
I can find surface areas of composite figures involving pyramids and cones.	1 2 3 4	

Name_____ Date_____

12.4 Review & Refresh

In Exercises 1 and 2, find the indicated measure.

1. area of a circle with a radius of 8 meters

2. diameter of a circle with an area of 324π square inches

In Exercises 3–7, find the volume of the prism or cylinder.

3.

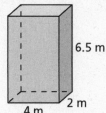

6.5 m

4 m 2 m

4.

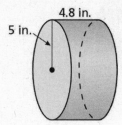

4.8 in.

5 in.

5.

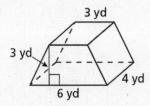

3 yd

3 yd

6 yd

4 yd

6.

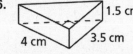

1.5 cm

4 cm 3.5 cm

7.

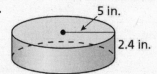

5 in.

2.4 in.

12.4 Review & Refresh (continued)

8. Two polygons are similar. The perimeter of one polygon is 78 feet. The ratio of corresponding side lengths is $\frac{5}{3}$. Find two possible perimeters of the other polygon.

9. You cut canned cranberry sauce parallel to its bases. Find the perimeter and area of the cross section formed by the cut.

1.6 in.

10. Tell whether $\overset{\frown}{XY} \cong \overset{\frown}{YZ}$. Explain why or why not.

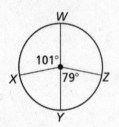

W

101°

X

79°

Z

Y

12.4 Self-Assessment

Use the scale to rate your understanding of the learning target and the success criteria.

1 I do not understand yet.	**2** I can do it with help.	**3** I can do it on my own.	**4** I can teach someone else.

	Rating	Date
12.4 Volumes of Prisms and Cylinders		
Learning Target: Find and use volumes of prisms and cylinders.	1 2 3 4	
I can find volumes of prisms and cylinders.	1 2 3 4	
I can solve real-life problems involving volumes of prisms and cylinders.	1 2 3 4	
I can find volumes of similar prisms and similar cylinders.	1 2 3 4	

Name_____ Date_____

1. Solve the triangle.

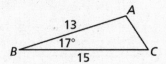

2. The diagram shows the portion of Earth visible to a camera on a weather balloon about 63 miles above Earth at point *B*. Earth's radius is approximately 4000 miles. Find $m\overarc{AC}$.

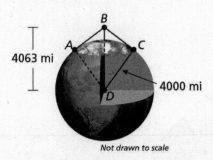

Not drawn to scale

3. Find the volume of the pyramid.

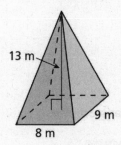

4. Find the missing dimension of the cylinder.

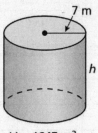

$V = 1847 \text{ m}^3$

12.5 Review & Refresh (continued)

5. In rectangle $ABCD$, $AC = 4x + 15$ and $BD = 7x - 9$. Find the lengths of the diagonals of $ABCD$.

6. Determine whether $\overline{RT} \parallel \overline{QU}$. Explain.

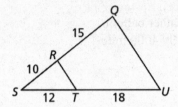

In Exercises 7 and 8, find the surface area of the solid.

7. a right cone with a radius of 6 feet and a height of 17 feet

8.

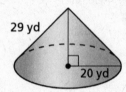

12.5 Self-Assessment

Use the scale to rate your understanding of the learning target and the success criteria.

| 1 | I do not understand yet. | 2 | I can do it with help. | 3 | I can do it on my own. | 4 | I can teach someone else. |

	Rating	Date
12.5 Volumes of Pyramids and Cones		
Learning Target: Find and use volumes of pyramids and cones.	1 2 3 4	
I can find volumes of pyramids and cones.	1 2 3 4	
I can use volumes of pyramids and cones to find measures.	1 2 3 4	
I can find volumes of similar pyramids and similar cones.	1 2 3 4	
I can find volumes of composite solids containing pyramids or cones.	1 2 3 4	

12.6 Review & Refresh

1. Show that a quadrilateral with vertices $W(1, 12)$, $X(7, 2)$, $Y(6, -7)$, and $Z(-6, 13)$ is a trapezoid. Then decide whether it is isosceles.

2. The cylinders are similar. Find the volume of cylinder B.

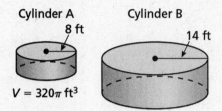

Cylinder A   Cylinder B

8 ft   14 ft

$V = 320\pi$ ft³

3. Find the surface area and the volume of the sphere.

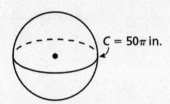

$C = 50\pi$ in.

4. Find the volume of the composite solid.

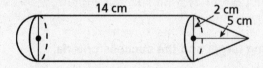

14 cm   2 cm
               5 cm

5. Find the surface area and the volume of the solid.

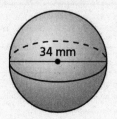

34 mm

12.6   Review & Refresh (continued)

6. Decide whether enough information is given to prove that △*PQS* and △*RQS* are congruent. Explain.

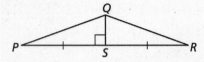

In Exercises 7 and 8, find the value of *x*. Write your answer in simplest form.

7.
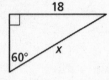

8.

12.6   Self-Assessment

Use the scale to rate your understanding of the learning target and the success criteria.

| 1 | I do not understand yet. | 2 | I can do it with help. | 3 | I can do it on my own. | 4 | I can teach someone else. |

	Rating	Date
12.6 Surface Areas and Volumes of Spheres		
Learning Target: Find and use surface areas and volumes of spheres.	1 2 3 4	
I can find surface areas of spheres.	1 2 3 4	
I can find volumes of spheres.	1 2 3 4	
I can find the volumes of composite solids.	1 2 3 4	

12.7 Review & Refresh

1. Find sin D, sin E, cos D, and cos E. Write each answer as a fraction and as a decimal.

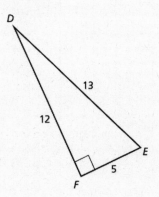

2. Find the value of x. Write your answer in simplest form.

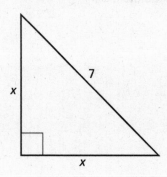

3. The pyramids are similar. Find the volume of pyramid B.

Pyramid A   Pyramid B

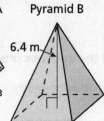

4 m   6.4 m

$V = 12$ m³

4. Steel has a density of about 7.8 grams per cubic centimeter. A steel rod has a diameter of $\frac{7}{16}$ inch and a length of 9 inches. Find the mass of the steel rod.

12.7 Review & Refresh (continued)

5. Find the surface area and the volume of the sphere.

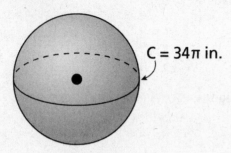

$C = 34\pi$ in.

6. Lead has a density of about 11.34 grams per cubic centimeter. The lead spacer shown has a radius of 5 centimeters and a height of 3 centimeters. Find the mass of the lead pedestal.

12.7 Self-Assessment

Use the scale to rate your understanding of the learning target and the success criteria.

| 1 | I do not understand yet. | 2 | I can do it with help. | 3 | I can do it on my own. | 4 | I can teach someone else. |

	Rating	Date
12.7 Modeling with Surface Area and Volume		
Learning Target: Understand the concept of density and modeling with volume.	1 2 3 4	
I can explain what density means.	1 2 3 4	
I can use the formula for density to solve problems.	1 2 3 4	
I can use geometric shapes to model objects.	1 2 3 4	
I can solve modeling problems.	1 2 3 4	

12.8 Review & Refresh

1. A circular region has a population of about 3.1 million people and a population density of about 9867 people per square mile. Find the radius of the region.

2. Sketch and describe the solid produced by rotating the figure around the given axis. Then find its surface area and volume.

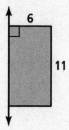

6

11

3. The diagram shows dimensions of a cork. Cork has a density of 0.24 gram per cubic centimeter. Find the mass of the cork.

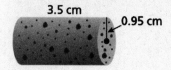

3.5 cm

0.95 cm

4. Find the value of x. Tell whether the side lengths form a Pythagorean triple.

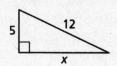

5

12

x

5. Find the surface area of the sphere.

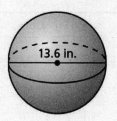

13.6 in.

12.8 Review & Refresh (continued)

6. Find the volume of the cone.

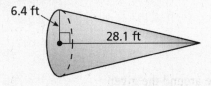

6.4 ft

28.1 ft

7. You are running on a circular path at a constant rate of 7.4 feet per second. The path is 0.75 mile in diameter. How long will it take you to run three complete laps?

8. Write an equation of a circle with center $C(-4, 3)$ and radius $r = 2$.

12.8 Self-Assessment

Use the scale to rate your understanding of the learning target and the success criteria.

| **1** I do not understand yet. | **2** I can do it with help. | **3** I can do it on my own. | **4** I can teach someone else. |

	Rating	Date
12.8 Solids of Revolution		
Learning Target: Sketch and use solids of revolution.	1 2 3 4	
I can sketch and describe solids of revolution.	1 2 3 4	
I can find surface areas and volumes of solids of revolution.	1 2 3 4	
I can form solids of revolution in the coordinate plane.	1 2 3 4	

Name_____ Date_____

Chapter 12 Chapter Self-Assessment

Use the scale to rate your understanding of the learning target and the success criteria.

| **1** I do not understand yet. | **2** I can do it with help. | **3** I can do it on my own. | **4** I can teach someone else. |

	Rating	Date
Chapter 12 Surface Area and Volume		
Learning Target: Understand surface area and volume.	1　2　3　4	
I can describe attributes of solids.	1　2　3　4	
I can find surface areas and volumes of solids.	1　2　3　4	
I can find missing dimensions of solids.	1　2　3　4	
I can solve real-life problems involving surface area and volume.	1　2　3　4	
12.1 Cross Sections of Solids		
Learning Target: Describe and draw cross sections.	1　2　3　4	
I can describe attributes of solids.	1　2　3　4	
I can describe and draw cross sections.	1　2　3　4	
I can solve real-life problems involving cross sections.	1　2　3　4	
12.2 Surface Areas of Prisms and Cylinders		
Learning Target: Find and use surface areas of prisms and cylinders.	1　2　3　4	
I can find surface areas of prisms and cylinders.	1　2　3　4	
I can solve real-life problems involving surface areas of prisms and cylinders.	1　2　3　4	
I can find surface areas of similar prisms and similar cylinders.	1　2　3　4	
12.3 Surface Areas of Pyramids and Cones		
Learning Target: Find and use surface areas of pyramids and cones.	1　2　3　4	
I can find surface areas of pyramids and cones.	1　2　3　4	
I can find surface areas of similar pyramids and similar cones.	1　2　3　4	
I can find surface areas of composite figures involving pyramids and cones.	1　2　3　4	

Chapter 12 — Chapter Self-Assessment (continued)

	Rating	Date
12.4 Volumes of Prisms and Cylinders		
Learning Target: Find and use volumes of prisms and cylinders.	1 2 3 4	
I can find volumes of prisms and cylinders.	1 2 3 4	
I can solve real-life problems involving volumes of prisms and cylinders.	1 2 3 4	
I can find volumes of similar prisms and similar cylinders.	1 2 3 4	
12.5 Volumes of Pyramids and Cones		
Learning Target: Find and use volumes of pyramids and cones.	1 2 3 4	
I can find volumes of pyramids and cones.	1 2 3 4	
I can use volumes of pyramids and cones to find measures.	1 2 3 4	
I can find volumes of similar pyramids and similar cones.	1 2 3 4	
I can find volumes of composite solids containing pyramids or cones.	1 2 3 4	
12.6 Surface Areas and Volumes of Spheres		
Learning Target: Find and use surface areas and volumes of spheres.	1 2 3 4	
I can find surface areas of spheres.	1 2 3 4	
I can find volumes of spheres.	1 2 3 4	
I can find the volumes of composite solids.	1 2 3 4	
12.7 Modeling with Surface Area and Volume		
Learning Target: Understand the concept of density and modeling with volume.	1 2 3 4	
I can explain what density means.	1 2 3 4	
I can use the formula for density to solve problems.	1 2 3 4	
I can use geometric shapes to model objects.	1 2 3 4	
I can solve modeling problems.	1 2 3 4	
12.8 Solids of Revolution		
Learning Target: Sketch and use solids of revolution.	1 2 3 4	
I can sketch and describe solids of revolution.	1 2 3 4	
I can find surface areas and volumes of solids of revolution.	1 2 3 4	
I can form solids of revolution in the coordinate plane.	1 2 3 4	

Chapter 12 B.E.S.T. Test Prep

1. What is the volume, in cubic millimeters, of the sphere with a surface area of 2304π square millimeters? Round the answer to the nearest tenth.

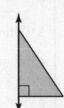

2. A circular region with an 8-mile radius has a population density of 942 people per square mile. How many people live in the region?

3. What solid is produced by rotating the figure around the given axis?

   Ⓐ square pyramid

   Ⓑ cone

   Ⓒ triangular pyramid

   Ⓓ triangular prism

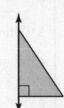

4. What is the volume of the composite solid?

   Ⓐ about 54.8 in.³

   Ⓑ about 73.7 in.³

   Ⓒ about 111.4 in.³

   Ⓓ about 186.8 in.³

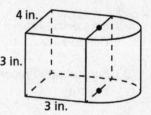

5. Which of the following triangles are similar to $\triangle ABC$? Select all that apply.

   Ⓐ
   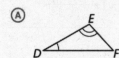

   Ⓒ
   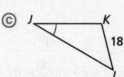

   Ⓑ

   Ⓓ
   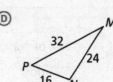

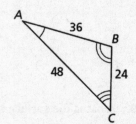

Chapter 12 **B.E.S.T. Test Prep** (continued)

6. What is the value of *y* that makes the quadrilateral a parallelogram?

Ⓐ 9

Ⓑ 10

Ⓒ 20

Ⓓ 24

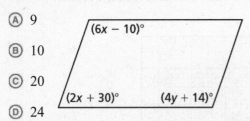

7. The surface area of the cone is 703.7 square meters. What is the height of the cone?

Ⓐ 13.7 m

Ⓑ 14 m

Ⓒ 24 m

Ⓓ 25 m

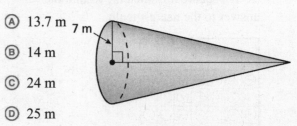

8. Which definitions and properties can you use to complete the proof? Select all that apply.

Ⓐ Subtraction Property of Equality

Ⓑ Transitive Property of Congruence

Ⓒ Division Property of Equality

Ⓓ Symmetric Property of Congruence

Ⓔ Substitution Property of Equality

Ⓕ Definition of segment bisector

Given $QS = TV$, $\overrightarrow{RU}$ bisects $\overline{QS}$ and $\overline{TV}$

Prove $RS = TU$

STATEMENTS	REASONS
1. $QS = TV$, $\overrightarrow{RU}$ bisects $\overline{QS}$ and $\overline{TV}$	1. Given
2. $\overline{QR} \cong \overline{RS}$, $\overline{TU} \cong \overline{UV}$	2. _____
3. $QR = RS$, $TU = UV$	3. Definition of congruent segments
4. $QS = QR + RS$ $TV = TU + UV$	4. Segment Addition Postulate
5. $QR + RS = TU + UV$	5. _____
6. $RS + RS = TU + TU$	6. _____
7. $2RS = 2TU$	7. Distributive Property
8. $RS = TU$	8. _____

9. What is the surface area of the hemisphere?

Ⓐ about 265.5 in.²

Ⓑ about 398.2 in.²

Ⓒ about 1061.9 in.²

Ⓓ about 1592.8 in.²

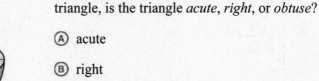

10. If the segment lengths 8, 11, and 16 form a triangle, is the triangle *acute*, *right*, or *obtuse*?

Ⓐ acute

Ⓑ right

Ⓒ obtuse

Ⓓ The segment lengths do not form a triangle.

Chapter 12 **B.E.S.T. Test Prep** (continued)

11. Which of the following are polyhedra? Select all that apply.

Ⓐ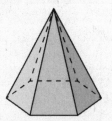

Ⓒ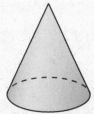

Ⓑ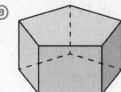

Ⓓ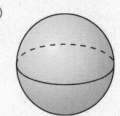

12. The volume of the cone is 152.1 cubic centimeters. What is the surface area of the cone?

Ⓐ about 221.2 cm²

Ⓑ about 561.1 cm²

Ⓒ about 763.7 cm²

Ⓓ about 974.5 cm²

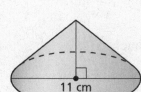
11 cm

13. A pyramid with a square base has a volume of 96 cubic feet and a height of 8 feet. What is the side length of the base?

Ⓐ $2\sqrt{3}$ ft

Ⓑ 6 ft

Ⓒ 18 ft

Ⓓ 36 ft

14. The pyramids are similar. What is the volume of pyramid B?

Ⓐ 122.88 in.³

Ⓑ 153.6 in.³

Ⓒ 192 in.³

Ⓓ 300 in.³

Pyramid A   Pyramid B

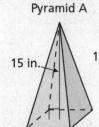 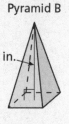

15 in.   12 in.

$V = 240$ in.³

15. Describe the shape formed by the intersection of the plane and the solid.

_____

Chapter 12

B.E.S.T. Test Prep (continued)

16. What is $m\widehat{AE}$?

Ⓐ 18°

Ⓑ 54°

Ⓒ 72°

Ⓓ 108°

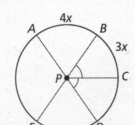

17. What is tan F?

Ⓐ $\dfrac{7}{2}$

Ⓑ $\dfrac{3\sqrt{5}}{2}$

Ⓒ $\dfrac{3\sqrt{5}}{7}$

Ⓓ $\dfrac{2\sqrt{5}}{15}$

18. What is the value of x that makes $m \parallel n$?

Ⓐ 9.25

Ⓑ 13.25

Ⓒ 14

Ⓓ 16

19. What are the possible values of x?

Ⓐ $0 < x < 6$

Ⓑ $\dfrac{7}{3} < x < 6$

Ⓒ $x > 6$

Ⓓ $x = 6$

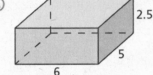

20. Which of the following solids has the greatest volume?

Ⓐ

Ⓒ

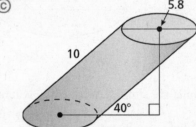

Ⓑ

Ⓓ

21. The diagram shows the dimensions of a bar of silver. Silver has a density of about 10.49 grams per cubic centimeter. What is the mass of the bar of silver?

Ⓐ 1.7 kg

Ⓒ 63.6 kg

Ⓑ 15.7 kg

Ⓓ 1730.9 kg

Geometry Post-Course Test

1. Which congruence transformations map $\triangle XYZ$ to $\triangle X''Y''Z''$? Select all that apply.

   Ⓐ reflection in the y-axis, followed by a reflection in the x-axis

   Ⓑ rotation of 90° counterclockwise about the origin, followed by a reflection in the y-axis

   Ⓒ rotation of 270° counterclockwise about the origin, followed by a reflection in the x-axis

   Ⓓ reflection in the x-axis, followed by a reflection in the y-axis

   Ⓔ reflection in the x-axis, followed by a rotation of 90° counterclockwise about the origin

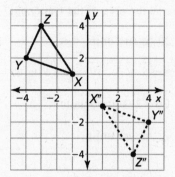

2. What is the perimeter of the parallelogram?

   Ⓐ 12 units

   Ⓑ 15 units

   Ⓒ 30 units

   Ⓓ 44 units

3. What is $m\overset{\frown}{BD}$?

   Ⓐ 11°

   Ⓑ 18°

   Ⓒ 24°

   Ⓓ 32°

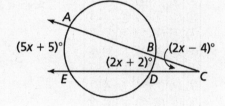

4. Points B and D are points of tangency. What are the values of x? Select all that apply.

   Ⓐ −3

   Ⓑ −2

   Ⓒ 2

   Ⓓ 3

   Ⓔ 6

   Ⓕ 16

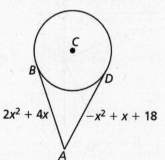

5. What is another name for $\overleftrightarrow{CD}$? Select all that apply.

   Ⓐ $\overrightarrow{DC}$

   Ⓑ $\overrightarrow{AB}$

   Ⓒ line m

   Ⓓ $\overrightarrow{CE}$

   Ⓔ line n

   Ⓕ $\overleftrightarrow{ED}$

6. What is an equation of the perpendicular bisector of the segment with endpoints $M(-3, 8)$ and $N(1, -2)$?

_____

Geometry **Post-Course Test** (continued)

7. What is the area of the trapezoid?

Ⓐ 20 square units

Ⓑ $4\sqrt{5} + 4\sqrt{10}$ square units

Ⓒ $20\sqrt{2}$ square units

Ⓓ 40 square units

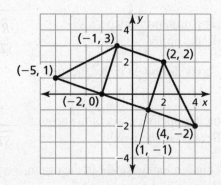

8. The triangles are similar. What is the area (in square inches) of triangle *A*?

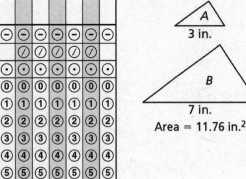

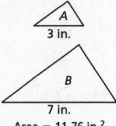

A
3 in.

B
7 in.
Area = 11.76 in.²

9. What is the area (in square units) of the shaded region? Round to the nearest hundredth.

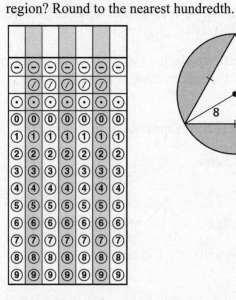

10. △*LMN* has vertices *L*(1, 0), *M*(0, 3), and *N*(2, 2). Which graph shows the image of △*LMN* after a dilation with a scale factor of 3, followed by a translation 4 units down and 2 units left?

Ⓐ
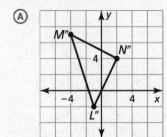

Ⓒ
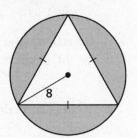

Ⓑ
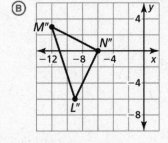

Ⓓ
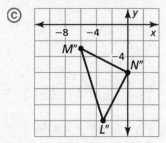

Geometry **Post-Course Test** (continued)

11. Which reason justifies the third statement in the proof?

Ⓐ SAS Congruence Theorem

Ⓑ SSS Congruence Theorem

Ⓒ ASA Congruence Theorem

Ⓓ AAS Congruence Theorem

Given $\overline{QT} \cong \overline{SR}$, $\overline{QR} \cong \overline{ST}$
Prove $\triangle QRS \cong \triangle STQ$

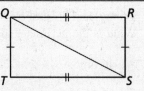

STATEMENTS	REASONS
1. $\overline{QT} \cong \overline{SR}$, $\overline{QR} \cong \overline{ST}$	1. Given
2. $\overline{QS} \cong \overline{QS}$	2. Reflexive Property of Segment Congruence
3. $\triangle QRS \cong \triangle STQ$	3._____

12. What is $m\angle WYZ$ in rhombus $WXYZ$?

Ⓐ 41°

Ⓑ 49°

Ⓒ 82°

Ⓓ 98°

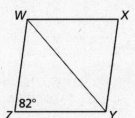

13. Complete the congruence statement.

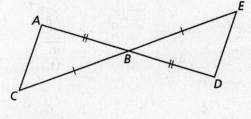

$\triangle ABC \cong$ _____

14. Which of the following statements are incorrect? Select all that apply.

Ⓐ The centroid of a triangle is always inside the triangle.

Ⓑ The circumcenter of a triangle is equidistant from the vertices of the triangle.

Ⓒ The angle bisectors of a triangle intersect at the incenter.

Ⓓ The three medians of a triangle intersect at the circumcenter.

Ⓔ The orthocenter of a triangle is always inside the triangle.

15. Which property illustrates the statement?
If $a = b$, then $b = a$.

Ⓐ Symmetric Property of Equality

Ⓑ Reflexive Property of Equality

Ⓒ Transitive Property of Equality

Ⓓ Multiplication Property of Equality

16. What is the diameter of a circle with an area of 824.5 square inches?

Ⓐ about 8.1 in.

Ⓑ about 16.2 in.

Ⓒ about 28.7 in.

Ⓓ about 32.4 in.

Geometry **Post-Course Test** (continued)

17. Triangles *ABC* and *DEF* are similar. The longest side of △*ABC* is 45 units. What is the perimeter of △*ABC*?

Ⓐ 46 units

Ⓑ 58.5 units

Ⓒ 103.5 units

Ⓓ 207 units

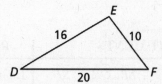

18. ∠*ABC* and ∠*LMN* are supplementary angles, $m\angle ABC = (3x - 15)°$, and $m\angle LMN = (5x + 9)°$. What is $m\angle ABC$?

Ⓐ 21°

Ⓑ 54.75°

Ⓒ 69°

Ⓓ 125.25°

19. What is the value of *z*?

Ⓐ 5

Ⓑ 6

Ⓒ 7

Ⓓ 8

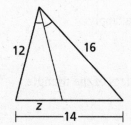

20. What is the measure of the exterior angle?

Ⓐ 85°

Ⓑ 95°

Ⓒ 122°

Ⓓ 153°

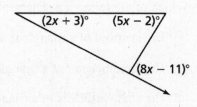

21. What is the length of $\overline{AB}$?

Ⓐ 4.6

Ⓑ 12.6

Ⓒ 14.9

Ⓓ 19.5

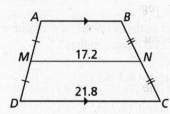

22. What is the height of the pyramid?

Ⓐ 1 ft

Ⓑ 3 ft

Ⓒ 6 ft

Ⓓ 9 ft

Volume = 252 ft³

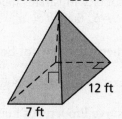

Geometry **Post-Course Test** (continued)

23. What is the value of *y*?

Ⓐ 2

Ⓑ 3

Ⓒ 4

Ⓓ 8

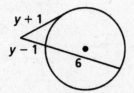

24. What can you conclude from the diagram?

Ⓐ *DE = GH*

Ⓑ *DE > GH*

Ⓒ *DE < GH*

Ⓓ No conclusion can be made.

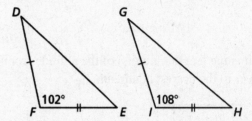

25. What is the value of *b*?

Ⓐ $2\sqrt{7}$

Ⓑ $4\sqrt{3}$

Ⓒ $2\sqrt{21}$

Ⓓ $4\sqrt{7}$

26. Which side lengths form an acute triangle?

Ⓐ 5, 12, 13

Ⓑ 8, 10, 14

Ⓒ 6, 7, 11

Ⓓ 7, 11, 12

27. What is the inverse of the conditional statement?
Conditional Statement: If a polygon is regular, then its sides are congruent.

Ⓐ If a polygon's sides are congruent, then it is regular.

Ⓑ If a polygon is not regular, then its sides are not congruent.

Ⓒ If a polygon's sides are not congruent, then it is not regular.

Ⓓ A polygon is regular if and only if its sides are congruent.

28. What is the slope-intercept form of the equation of the line passing through the point $(6, -1)$ that is parallel to the line $2x - 3y = 8$?

_____

Geometry **Post-Course Test** (continued)

29. The midpoint of $\overline{CD}$ is $M(-1, 7)$ and one endpoint of $\overline{CD}$ is $D(4, 5)$. What are the coordinates of C?

    Ⓐ $(-6, 9)$

    Ⓑ $(9, 3)$

    Ⓒ $(-10, 4)$

    Ⓓ $(1.5, 6)$

30. What is the length (in units) of the altitude from vertex A to $\overline{XZ}$? Round your answer to the nearest hundredth.

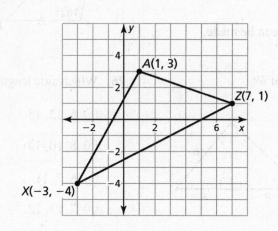

31. What is the radius of $\odot C$?

    Ⓐ 2

    Ⓑ 5

    Ⓒ 12

    Ⓓ 13

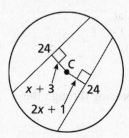

Geometry **Post-Course Test** (continued)

32. What is sin A?

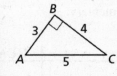

33. A quarter of a circle is removed from a square, as shown. What is the perimeter (in centimeters) of the shaded region? Round to the nearest tenth.

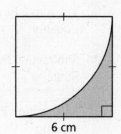

6 cm

34. The endpoints of a diameter of a circle are $(5, -2)$ and $(11, 8)$. What is the standard equation of the circle?

_____

35. What is MN?

Ⓐ 7

Ⓑ 13

Ⓒ 14

Ⓓ 26

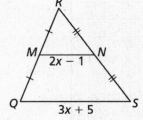

36. What is $m\angle Y$?

Ⓐ 40°

Ⓑ 50°

Ⓒ 80°

Ⓓ 160°

Geometry **Post-Course Test** (continued)

37. Which of the following properties and definitions are needed to complete the proof? Select all that apply.

Ⓐ Transitive Property of Equality

Ⓑ Subtraction Property of Equality

Ⓒ Substitution Property of Equality

Ⓓ Definition of right angle

Ⓔ Symmetric Property of Equality

Ⓕ Definition of angle bisector

Given $\angle DBE$ is a right angle.
Prove $\angle ABD$ and $\angle CBE$ are complementary.

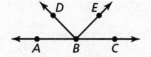

STATEMENTS	REASONS
1. $\angle DBE$ is a right angle.	1. Given
2. $m\angle DBE = 90°$	2. _____
3. $m\angle ABD + m\angle DBE$ $+ m\angle CBE = 180°$	3. Angle Addition Postulate
4. $m\angle ABD + 90°$ $+ m\angle CBE = 180°$	4. _____
5. $m\angle ABD + m\angle CBE = 90°$	5. _____
6. $\angle ABD$ and $\angle CBE$ are complementary.	6. Definition of complementary angles

38 What is the sum of x and y?

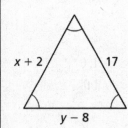

39. What is the sum (in degrees) of the measures of the interior angles of a convex 35-gon?

40. Two sides of a triangle have lengths 3 centimeters and 10 centimeters. Write an inequality to represent the possible lengths x (in centimeters) of the third side.

_____

Geometry **Post-Course Test** (continued)

41. What type of angle pair are ∠8 and ∠9?

Ⓐ corresponding angles

Ⓑ alternate interior angles

Ⓒ alternate exterior angles

Ⓓ consecutive interior angles

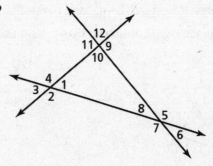

42. What additional information do you need to prove that $\triangle WXY \cong \triangle WZY$ by the ASA Congruence Theorem?

Ⓐ $\angle X \cong \angle Z$

Ⓑ $\angle WYX \cong \angle WYZ$

Ⓒ $\overline{WX} \cong \overline{WZ}$

Ⓓ $\overline{XY} \cong \overline{ZY}$

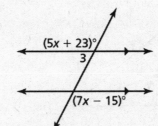

43. What is $m\angle 3$?

Ⓐ 62°

Ⓑ $85.\overline{3}°$

Ⓒ $94.\overline{6}°$

Ⓓ 118°

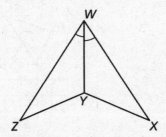

44. Three vertices of a parallelogram are $(-1, 5), (3, 2),$ and $(1, 0).$ Which of the following could be the fourth vertex of the parallelogram? Select all that apply.

Ⓐ $(-3, 3)$

Ⓑ $(5, -3)$

Ⓒ $(-5, 1)$

Ⓓ $(1, 7)$

Ⓔ $(-7, 6)$

Geometry **Post-Course Test** (continued)

45. △*ABC* has vertices *A*(3, −5), *B*(1, −4), and *C*(4, −2). Which graph shows the image of △*ABC*
after a reflection in the *y*-axis, followed by a rotation of 270° counterclockwise about the origin?

Ⓐ
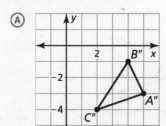

Ⓒ
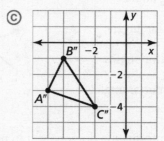

Ⓑ
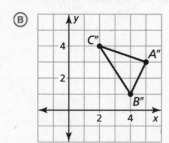

Ⓓ
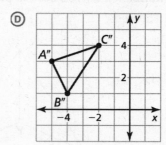

46. Point *N* is the incenter of △*QRP*, *NY* = 5*x* + 7, and *NZ* = 8*x* − 8. What is *NX*?

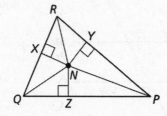

47. What is the volume of the cylinder?

Ⓐ about 2414.7 cm³

Ⓑ about 6281.6 cm³

Ⓒ about 9076.3 cm³

Ⓓ about 36,305.0 cm³

48. *m*∠*XYZ* = 130°. What is *m*∠*WYX*?

Ⓐ 20°

Ⓑ 56°

Ⓒ 65°

Ⓓ 74°

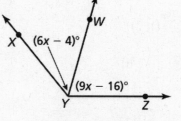

Correlation to Florida's B.E.S.T. Standards

Chapter 1 B.E.S.T. Test Prep

1. MA.6.NSO.1.4
2. MA.912.AR.10.4
3. MA.912.GR.3.4
4. MA.6.AR.1.3
5. MA.912.GR.3.1
6. MA.912.GR.3.4
7. MA.912.NSO.1.1
8. MA.912.AR.4.2
9. MA.912.AR.9.1
10. MA.912.GR.1.1
11. MA.912.AR.3.4
12. MA.912.AR.2.2
13. MA.912.GR.3.1
14. MA.912.GR.1.1
15. MA.912.AR.7.2
16. MA.6.DP.1.2
17. MA.4.GR.1.1, MA.4.GR.1.2
18. MA.912.GR.1.1
19. MA.912.AR.7.1
20. MA.912.GR.4.5
21. MA.912.GR.1.1

Chapter 2 B.E.S.T. Test Prep

1. MA.912.GR.1.1
2. MA.912.GR.3.1
3. MA.912.AR.10.3
4. MA.912.GR.1.1
5. MA.912.LT.4.3
6. MA.912.GR.3.3
7. MA.912.AR.1.7

8. MA.912.GR.1.1
9. MA.912.F.3.7
10. MA.912.LT.4.10
11. MA.912.GR.1.1
12. MA.912.NSO.1.1
13. MA.912.GR.3.4
14. MA.912.AR.2.6
15. MA.912.AR.1.2
16. MA.912.LT.4.3

Chapter 3 B.E.S.T. Test Prep

1. MA.912.GR.1.1
2. MA.912.LT.4.3
3. MA.912.GR.1.1
4. MA.912.GR.1.1
5. MA.912.GR.1.1
6. MA.912.GR.1.1
7. MA.912.GR.3.1
8. MA.912.GR.1.1
9. MA.912.GR.1.1
10. MA.912.LT.4.9, MA.912.LT.4.3
11. MA.912.GR.1.1
12. MA.912.GR.3.3
13. MA.912.GR.3.4
14. MA.912.GR.1.1
15. MA.912.GR.3.3
16. MA.912.GR.1.1
17. MA.912.GR.1.1

Chapter 4 B.E.S.T. Test Prep

1. MA.912.GR.2.1
2. MA.912.AR.10.4

3. MA.912.GR.1.1
4. MA.912.GR.2.2
5. MA.912.GR.2.3
6. MA.912.GR.1.1
7. MA.912.GR.2.1
8. MA.912.GR.2.3
9. MA.912.GR.2.5
10. MA.912.GR.3.4
11. MA.912.GR.3.1, MA.912.GR.3.4
12. MA.912.GR.1.1
13. MA.912.GR.2.8
14. MA.912.GR.1.1
15. MA.912.GR.1.1
16. MA.912.GR.2.1, MA.912.GR.2.5
17. MA.912.GR.3.3
18. MA.912.GR.2.2

Chapter 5 B.E.S.T. Test Prep

1. MA.912.GR.3.3
2. MA.912.GR.1.5
3. MA.912.GR.3.4
4. MA.912.GR.3.3
5. MA.912.GR.1.3
6. MA.912.GR.3.1
7. MA.912.GR.2.9
8. MA.912.GR.1.4
9. MA.912.GR.1.1
10. MA.912.T.1.2
11. MA.912.GR.1.1
12. MA.912.GR.1.3
13. MA.912.GR.1.1

14. MA.912.GR.1.2
15. MA.912.GR.1.6
16. MA.912.GR.1.1
17. MA.912.GR.1.2
18. MA.912.GR.1.2
19. MA.912.GR.2.1
20. MA.912.GR.3.4
21. MA.912.GR.1.2

Chapter 6 B.E.S.T. Test Prep

1. MA.912.GR.1.1
2. MA.912.GR.1.1
3. MA.912.GR.1.3
4. MA.912.GR.1.3
5. MA.912.GR.1.6
6. MA.912.GR.1.3
7. MA.912.GR.1.6
8. MA.912.GR.1.3
9. MA.912.GR.3.3
10. MA.912.GR.1.6
11. MA.912.GR.1.3
12. MA.912.GR.1.3
13. MA.912.GR.2.1
14. MA.912.GR.1.3
15. MA.912.GR.1.3
16. MA.912.GR.1.1
17. MA.912.GR.1.3
18. MA.912.GR.1.2
19. MA.912.GR.1.3
20. MA.912.GR.2.2
21. MA.912.GR.3.1
22. MA.912.LT.4.3

Correlation to Florida's B.E.S.T. Standards (continued)

Chapter 7 B.E.S.T. Test Prep

1. MA.912.GR.1.5
2. MA.912.GR.1.3
3. MA.912.GR.1.3
4. MA.912.GR.1.2, MA.912.GR.1.6
5. MA.912.GR.1.4
6. preparing for MA.912.GR.1.4
7. MA.912.GR.1.4
8. preparing for MA.8.GR.1.4
9. MA.912.GR.1.4
10. MA.912.GR.1.3
11. MA.912.GR.1.4
12. MA.912.GR.1.4
13. MA.912.GR.1.3
14. MA.912.GR.2.1
15. MA.912.GR.2.5, MA.912.GR.3.4
16. MA.912.GR.1.3, MA.912.GR.3.3
17. MA.912.GR.1.4
18. MA.912.GR.1.1
19. MA.912.GR.1.1
20. MA.912.GR.1.1
21. MA.912.GR.2.3
22. MA.912.GR.1.2

Chapter 8 B.E.S.T. Test Prep

1. MA.912.GR.1.6
2. MA.912.GR.1.3
3. MA.912.GR.1.2
4. MA.912.GR.1.6
5. MA.912.GR.1.6
6. MA.912.GR.1.3
7. MA.912.GR.1.4, MA.912.GR.1.5
8. MA.912.GR.1.4
9. MA.912.GR.1.1
10. MA.912.GR.1.6
11. MA.912.GR.1.3
12. MA.912.GR.1.3
13. MA.912.GR.1.6, MA.912.GR.3.4
14. MA.912.GR.2.9
15. MA.912.GR.1.1
16. MA.912.GR.2.1
17. MA.912.GR.1.4
18. MA.912.GR.1.1
19. MA.912.GR.1.6
20. MA.912.GR.1.6
21. MA.912.GR.3.3

Chapter 9 B.E.S.T. Test Prep

1. MA.912.T.1.2
2. MA.912.GR.1.4
3. MA.912.GR.1.6
4. MA.912.GR.1.6
5. MA.912.GR.1.1
6. MA.912.GR.1.3
7. MA.912.T.1.3
8. MA.912.GR.1.1
9. MA.912.T.1.2
10. MA.912.T.1.4
11. MA.912.GR.1.6
12. MA.912.GR.1.3

13. MA.912.GR.1.1
14. MA.912.GR.2.2
15. MA.912.GR.1.6
16. MA.912.GR.1.6
17. MA.912.T.1.1
18. MA.912.T.1.1
19. MA.912.GR.1.3
20. MA.912.T.1.2
21. MA.912.T.1.4
22. MA.912.T.1.2
23. MA.912.GR.1.2

Chapter 10 B.E.S.T. Test Prep

1. MA.912.GR.6.1
2. MA.912.GR.1.4
3. MA.912.GR.7.2
4. MA.912.GR.6.2
5. MA.912.GR.1.5
6. MA.912.GR.1.2
7. MA.912.GR.6.1
8. MA.912.T.1.2
9. MA.912.GR.1.3
10. MA.912.GR.1.5
11. MA.912.GR.1.2, MA.912.GR.1.6
12. MA.912.GR.6.1
13. MA.912.GR.1.1
14. MA.912.GR.1.6
15. MA.912.T.1.2
16. MA.912.GR.6.3
17. MA.912.GR.6.2
18. MA.912.GR.6.1

19. MA.912.GR.6.1
20. MA.912.GR.6.1
21. MA.912.GR.7.3
22. MA.912.GR.6.2
23. MA.912.GR.1.3
24. MA.912.GR.2.5

Chapter 11 B.E.S.T. Test Prep

1. MA.912.GR.4.4
2. MA.912.GR.6.4
3. MA.912.GR.1.1
4. MA.912.GR.4.4
5. MA.912.GR.1.1
6. MA.912.GR.6.4
7. MA.912.GR.6.4, MA.912.GR.6.1
8. MA.912.GR.7.3
9. MA.912.GR.1.3
10. MA.912.GR.4.4
11. MA.912.GR.7.4
12. MA.912.T.1.2
13. MA.912.GR.6.4
14. MA.912.GR.4.4
15. MA.912.GR.4.4
16. MA.912.GR.3.4
17. MA.912.GR.6.4
18. MA.912.GR.3.3
19. MA.912.GR.7.3
20. MA.912.GR.1.6
21. MA.912.GR.2.5

Chapter 12 B.E.S.T. Test Prep

1. MA.912.GR.4.5

Correlation to Florida's B.E.S.T. Standards (continued)

2. MA.912.GR.4.4

3. MA.912.GR.4.2

4. MA.912.GR.4.5

5. MA.912.GR.1.6

6. MA.912.GR.1.4

7. MA.912.GR.4.6

8. MA.912.GR.1.1

9. MA.912.GR.4.6

10. MA.912.GR.1.3

11. MA.912.GR.4.2

12. MA.912.GR.4.5,
MA.912.GR.4.6

13. MA.912.GR.4.5

14. MA.912.GR.4.5

15. MA.912.GR.4.1

16. MA.912.GR.6.2

17. MA.912.T.1.1

18. MA.912.GR.1.1

19. MA.912.GR.1.3

20. MA.912.GR.4.5

21. MA.912.GR.4.5

Post-Course Test

1. MA.912.GR.2.3

2. MA.912.GR.1.4

3. MA.912.GR.6.2

4. MA.912.GR.6.1

5. preparing for
MA.912.GR.1.1

6. MA.912.GR.1.1

7. MA.912.GR.3.4

8. MA.912.GR.4.3

9. MA.912.GR.4.4,
MA.912.GR.6.3

10. MA.912.GR.2.5

11. MA.912.GR.1.2

12. MA.912.GR.4.4,
MA.912.GR.1.4

13. MA.912.GR.1.2

14. MA.912.GR.1.3

15. preparing for
MA.912.GR.1.1

16. MA.912.GR.4.4

17. MA.912.GR.1.6

18. preparing for
MA.912.GR.1.1

19. MA.912.GR.1.6

20. MA.912.GR.1.3

21. MA.912.GR.1.5

22. MA.912.GR.4.5

23. MA.912.GR.6.1

24. MA.912.GR.1.3

25. MA.912.GR.1.3,
MA.912.GR.1.6

26. MA.912.GR.1.3,
MA.912.T.1.2

27. MA.912.LT.4.3

28. MA.912.GR.3.3

29. MA.912.GR.3.3

30. MA.912.GR.3.3

31. MA.912.GR.6.1

32. MA.912.T.1.1

33. MA.912.GR.6.4

34. MA.912.GR.7.2

35. MA.912.GR.1.3

36. MA.912.GR.6.2

37. MA.912.GR.1.1

38. MA.912.GR.1.3

39. preparing for
MA.912.GR.1.4

40. MA.912.GR.1.3

41. preparing for
MA.912.GR.1.1

42. MA.912.GR.1.2

43. MA.912.GR.1.1

44. MA.912.GR.1.4

45. MA.912.GR.2.5

46. MA.912.GR.1.3

47. MA.912.GR.4.5

49. preparing for
MA.912.GR.1.1

Name_____ Date_____

Evidence-Based Scale Worksheets

Geometric Reasoning

MA.912.GR.1.1 Prove relationships and theorems about lines and angles. Solve mathematical and real-world problems involving postulates, relationships and theorems of lines and angles.

Circle the scale that best demonstrates your knowledge of the standard.

	Description	Evidence
4	**I can go beyond the standard.** • Teach someone else how to prove relationships and theorems about lines and angles and solve mathematical and real-world problems involving postulates, relationships and theorems of lines and angles.	Prove that when a transversal crosses parallel lines the alternate interior angles are congruent.
3	**I understand the entire standard.** • Prove relationships and theorems about lines and angles. • Solve mathematical and real-world problems involving postulates, relationships and theorems of lines and angles.	Prove that $\angle 1 \cong \angle 3$. 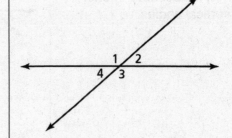

MA.912.GR.1.1 (continued)

	Description	**Evidence**
2	**I understand some parts, but not the entire standard.** • Use theorems about lines and angles to solve problems.	$m\angle 1 = 84°$; find the measures of all other angles in the diagram. 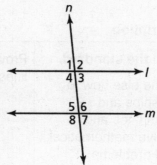
1	**I understand the basic skills needed to begin learning this standard.** • Identify pairs of corresponding, alternate interior, alternate exterior, consecutive interior and vertical angles.	Identify all pairs of angles of each type in the diagram. 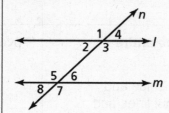 **a.** corresponding **b.** alternate interior **c.** alternate exterior **d.** consecutive interior **e.** vertical

Evidence-Based Scale Worksheets

Geometric Reasoning
MA.912.GR.1.2 Prove triangle congruence or similarity using Side-Side-Side, Side-Angle-Side, Angle-Side-Angle, Angle-Angle-Side, Angle-Angle and Hypotenuse-Leg.

Circle the scale that best demonstrates your knowledge of the standard.

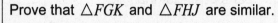

	Description	Evidence
4	**I can go beyond the standard.** • Teach someone else how to prove triangle congruence or similarity using Side-Side-Side, Side-Angle-Side, Angle-Side-Angle, Angle-Angle-Side, Angle-Angle and Hypotenuse-Leg.	Prove that $\triangle FGK$ and $\triangle FHJ$ are similar. 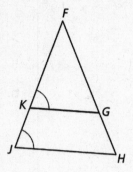
3	**I understand the entire standard.** • Prove triangle congruence or similarity using Side-Side-Side, Side-Angle-Side, Angle-Side-Angle, Angle-Angle-Side, Angle-Angle and Hypotenuse-Leg.	Prove that $\triangle ABE \cong \triangle DBC$. 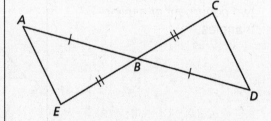

MA.912.GR.1.2 (continued)

	Description	Evidence
2	**I understand some parts, but not the entire standard.** • Find lengths and angle measures of corresponding parts of similar triangles.	$\triangle ABC$ and $\triangle DEF$ are similar, $m\angle A = 27°$, $AB = 6$, and $BC = 12$. **a.** What is $m\angle D$? **b.** If $DE = 9$, what is EF?
1	**I understand the basic skills needed to begin learning this standard.** • Identify corresponding parts of two congruent or similar triangles.	Identify the corresponding parts of $\triangle ABC$ and $\triangle DEF$. 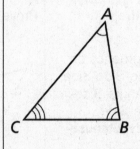 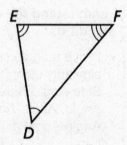 **a.** corresponding angles **b.** corresponding sides

Evidence-Based Scale Worksheets

Geometric Reasoning
MA.912.GR.1.3 Prove relationships and theorems about triangles. Solve mathematical and real-world problems involving postulates, relationships and theorems of triangles.

Circle the scale that best demonstrates your knowledge of the standard.

	Description	Evidence
4	**I can go beyond the standard.** • Teach someone else how to prove relationships and theorems about triangles.	Prove that the segment joining the midpoints of two sides of a triangle is parallel to the third side.
3	**I understand the entire standard.** • Prove relationships and theorems about triangles. Solve mathematical and real-world problems involving postulates, relationships and theorems of triangles.	Prove that $\angle A \cong \angle C$. 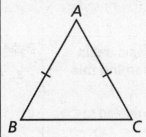

MA.912.GR.1.3 (continued)

	Description	Evidence
2	**I understand some parts, but not the entire standard.** • Find the measures of interior and exterior angles of a triangle.	Find each of the indicated angle measures. 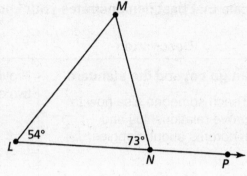 **a.** $m\angle M$ **b.** $m\angle MNP$
1	**I understand the basic skills needed to begin learning this standard.** • Define key terms related to triangles.	Define each of these terms. **a.** exterior angles **b.** base angles of an isosceles triangle **c.** midpoint **d.** median of a triangle

Name_____ Date_____

Geometric Reasoning
MA.912.GR.1.4 Prove relationships and theorems about parallelograms. Solve mathematical and real-world problems involving postulates, relationships and theorems of parallelograms.

Circle the scale that best demonstrates your knowledge of the standard.

	Description	**Evidence**
4	**I can go beyond the standard.** • Write a word problem involving postulates, relationships, and theorems of parallelograms.	Write a word problem involving postulates, relationships, and theorems of parallelograms.
3	**I understand the entire standard.** • Prove relationships and theorems about parallelograms. Solve mathematical and real-world problems involving postulates, relationships, and theorems of parallelograms.	Quadrilateral *ABCD* is a parallelogram. Prove that ∠*A* ≅ ∠*C*.

MA.912.GR.1.4 (continued)

	Description	Evidence
2	**I understand some parts, but not the entire standard.** • Use theorems about parallelograms to solve problems.	In parallelogram *EFGH*, $m\angle E = 62°$, $EF = 10$, and $FG = 14$. Find the measures of the remaining angles and sides.
1	**I understand the basic skills needed to begin learning this standard.** • Identify pairs of parallel sides of quadrilaterals.	Name all the pairs of parallel sides, if any, in each quadrilateral. **a.** trapezoid *ABCD* 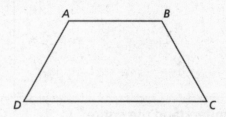 **b.** rectangle *EFGH*  **c.** kite *JKLM* 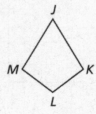

Name_____ Date_____

Geometric Reasoning
MA.912.GR.1.5 Prove relationships and theorems about trapezoids. Solve mathematical and real-world problems involving postulates, relationships and theorems of trapezoids.

Circle the scale that best demonstrates your knowledge of the standard.

	Description	Evidence
4	**I can go beyond the standard.** • Teach someone else how to solve mathematical and real-world problems involving postulates, relationships and theorems of trapezoids.	*ABCD* is a trapezoid. 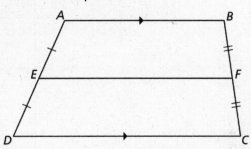 If *DC* = 17 and *EF* = 15, what is *AB*?
3	**I understand the entire standard.** • Prove relationships and theorems about trapezoids. Solve mathematical and real-world problems involving postulates, relationships and theorems of trapezoids.	*ABCD* is a trapezoid and $\overline{AB} \cong \overline{CD}$. Prove that $\overline{AC} \cong \overline{DB}$.

MA.912.GR.1.5 (continued)

	Description	Evidence
2	**I understand some parts, but not the entire standard.** • Use theorems about trapezoids to solve problems.	*EFGH* is an isosceles trapezoid. If $m\angle E = 74°$, find the measures of the other angles.
1	**I understand the basic skills needed to begin learning this standard.** • Recognize terms related to trapezoids.	Name the line segments that represent each term. 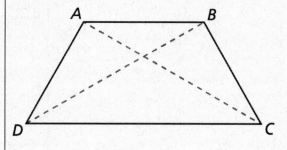 **a.** bases **b.** diagonals

Name_____ Date_____

Geometric Reasoning
MA.912.GR.1.6 Solve mathematical and real-world problems involving congruence or similarity in two-dimensional figures.

Circle the scale that best demonstrates your knowledge of the standard.

	Description	Evidence
4	**I can go beyond the standard.** • Teach someone else how to solve mathematical and real-world problems using congruence or similarity in a two-dimensional figure.	A carpenter is sketching plans for the roof of a shed. The frame will be an isosceles triangle with a base of 8 feet, and the two congruent sides will each measure 5 feet. On the sketch, the base measures 12 inches. What should the length of the congruent sides be to keep the sketch similar to the actual frame?
3	**I understand the entire standard.** • Solve mathematical and real-world problems involving congruence or similarity in two-dimensional figures.	In the diagram, $\triangle ABC \cong \triangle KLJ$. What is the measure of $m\angle J$? 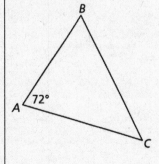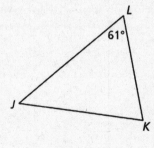

Name _____ Date _____

	Description	**Evidence**
2	**I understand some parts, but not the entire standard.** • Recognize that corresponding parts of congruent figures are congruent.	In the diagram, $\triangle ABC \cong \triangle FDE$. What is the length of DE? 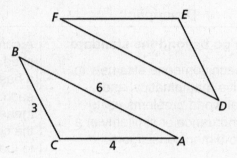
1	**I understand the basic skills needed to begin learning this standard.** • Recognize corresponding parts of congruent or similar figures.	Identify all of the congruent sides and angles in the diagram. 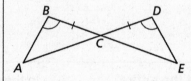

Name_____ Date_____

Geometric Reasoning
MA.912.GR.2.1 Given a preimage and image, describe the transformation and represent the transformation algebraically using coordinates.

Circle the scale that best demonstrates your knowledge of the standard.

	Description	Evidence
4	**I can go beyond the standard.** • Describe different combinations of transformations of a given preimage that can result in the same image.	Describe two different ways of transforming △EFG to obtain △E'F'G' 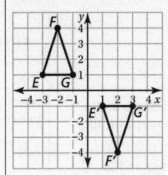
3	**I understand the entire standard.** • Given a preimage and image, describe the transformation and represent the transformation algebraically using coordinates.	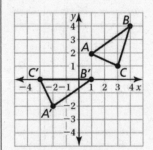 **a.** Describe the transformation from △ABC to △A'B'C'. **b.** Write a rule to describe the transformation.

MA.912.GR.2.1 (continued)

	Description	Evidence
2	**I understand some parts, but not the entire standard.** • Describe transformations given algebraically.	Describe each of these transformations. **a.** $(x, y) \rightarrow (x, -y)$ **b.** $(x, y) \rightarrow (2x, 2y)$ **c.** $(x, y) \rightarrow (x + 2, y - 5)$
1	**I understand the basic skills needed to begin learning this standard.** • Given a preimage and an image, recognize the type of transformation.	Identify each transformation as a dilation, translation, rotation or reflection. **a.** 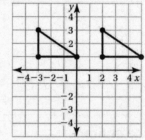 **b.** 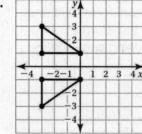 **c.** 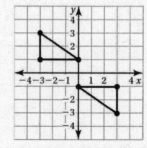

Evidence-Based Scale Worksheets

Geometric Reasoning
MA.912.GR.2.2 Identify transformations that do or do not preserve distance.

Circle the scale that best demonstrates your knowledge of the standard.

	Description	**Evidence**
4	**I can go beyond the standard.** • Teach someone to identify transformations that do or do not preserve distance.	$\triangle DEF$ is mapped onto $\triangle D'E'F'$ by the transformation $(x, y) \rightarrow (3x, 3y)$. **a.** Is $\overline{DE} \cong \overline{D'E'}$? **b.** Is $\angle DFE \cong \angle D'F'E'$?
3	**I understand the entire standard.** • Identify transformations that do or do not preserve distance.	$\triangle ABC$ is mapped onto $\triangle A'B'C'$ by the transformation $(x, y) \rightarrow (-x, -y)$. **a.** Is $\overline{AB} \cong \overline{A'B'}$? **b.** Is $\angle ABC \cong \angle A'B'C'$?

Name _____ Date _____

MA.912.GR.2.2 (continued)

	Description	Evidence
2	**I understand some parts, but not the entire standard.** • Know that translations, reflections and rotations preserve distance but dilations do not.	Indicate whether each of these transformations preserves distance. **a.** dilation **b.** reflection **c.** rotation **d.** translation
1	**I understand the basic skills needed to begin learning this standard.** • Define translations, rotations, reflections and dilations.	Define each of these transformations. **a.** translation **b.** rotation **c.** reflection **d.** dilation

Evidence-Based Scale Worksheets

Geometric Reasoning
MA.912.GR.2.3 Identify a sequence of transformations that will map a given figure onto itself or onto another congruent or similar figure.

Circle the scale that best demonstrates your knowledge of the standard.

	Description	Evidence
4	**I can go beyond the standard.** • Create a quadrilateral and describe the reflections and rotations that map it onto itself.	Create a quadrilateral that has rotational symmetry but not reflection symmetry. Describe the rotations that map the quadrilateral onto itself.
3	**I understand the entire standard.** • Identify a sequence of transformations that will map a given figure onto itself or onto another congruent or similar figure.	Describe the rotations and reflections that will map each figure onto itself. **a.** 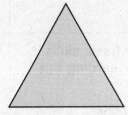 **b.** 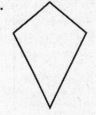 **c.** 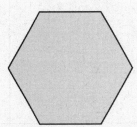

MA.912.GR.2.3 (continued)

	Description	Evidence
2	**I understand some parts, but not the entire standard.** • Describe a series of transformations that demonstrates the congruence of two figures.	Describe a series of transformations that shows that $\triangle ABC \cong \triangle DEF$. 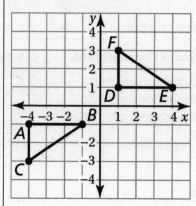
1	**I understand the basic skills needed to begin learning this standard.** • Identify rigid motions.	Identify if each transformation is a rigid motion. **a.** dilation **b.** reflection **c.** rotation **d.** translation

Evidence-Based Scale Worksheets

Geometric Reasoning

Ⓗ **MA.912.GR.2.4** Determine symmetries of reflection, symmetries of rotation and symmetries of translation of a geometric figure.

Circle the scale that best demonstrates your knowledge of the standard.

	Description	Evidence
4	**I can go beyond the standard.** • Design a figure that has a desired symmetry of reflection, rotation or translation.	Design a geometric figure that has reflection symmetry but not rotational symmetry.
3	**I understand the entire standard.** • Determine symmetries of reflection, symmetries of rotation and symmetries of translation of a geometric figure.	Identify all of the symmetries of reflection, roation and translation in a regular pentagon.

MA.912.GR.2.4 (continued)

	Description	**Evidence**
2	**I understand some parts, but not the entire standard.** • Identify figures with line symmetry, rotational symmetry and translation symmetry.	Identify whether each figure has line symmetry, rotational symmetry or translation symmetry. a.  b.  c. 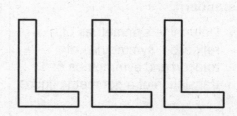
1	**I understand the basic skills needed to begin learning this standard.** • Define line symmetry and rotational symmetry.	Define the terms. a. line symmetry b. rotational symmetry

Name_____ Date_____

Geometric Reasoning
MA.912.GR.2.5 Given a geometric figure and a sequence of transformations, draw the transformed figure on a coordinate plane.

Circle the scale that best demonstrates your knowledge of the standard.

	Description	Evidence
4	**I can go beyond the standard.** • Teach someone how to draw a transformed figure on a coordinate plane.	Dilate quadrilateral *ABCD* by a scale factor of 2 from the point (0, 0), then rotate the figure 90° counterclockwise. Draw the transformed quadrilateral. 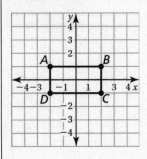
3	**I understand the entire standard.** • Given a geometric figure and a sequence of transformations, draw the transformed figure on a coordinate plane.	$\triangle JKL$ has vertices $J(3, 1)$, $K(3, 4)$, and $L(1, -2)$. Reflect $\triangle JKL$ across the x-axis and translate it 3 units left to form $\triangle J'K'L'$. Draw the transformed triangle.

Name _____ Date _____

	Description	**Evidence**
2	**I understand some parts, but not the entire standard.** • Given a geometric figure and one transformation, draw the transformed figure.	Draw a reflection of △DEF across line m. 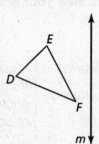
1	**I understand the basic skills needed to begin learning this standard.** • Identify transformations of figures.	Identify the transformation of △ABC to △A'B'C'. 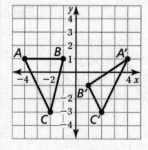

Evidence-Based Scale Worksheets

Geometric Reasoning

MA.912.GR.2.6 Apply rigid transformations to map one figure onto another to justify that the two figures are congruent.

Circle the scale that best demonstrates your knowledge of the standard.

	Description	Evidence
4	**I can go beyond the standard.** • Teach someone how to apply rigid transformations to map one figure onto another to justify that the two figures are congruent	Find a rigid transformation that can be used to show that quadrilateral *EFGH* and quadrilateral *JKLM* are congruent. 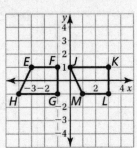
3	**I understand the entire standard.** • Apply rigid transformations to map one figure onto another to justify that the two figures are congruent.	Find a rigid transformation that can be used to show that $\triangle ABC \cong \triangle EFD$. 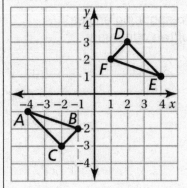

MA.912.GR.2.6 (continued)

	Description	**Evidence**
2	**I understand some parts, but not the entire standard.** • Use congruency to find angle measures and side lengths.	$\triangle DEF \cong \triangle PRQ$. Find the value of each measure. 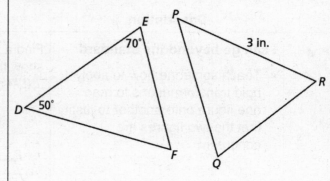 a. $m\angle P$ b. $m\angle R$ c. DE
1	**I understand the basic skills needed to begin learning this standard.** • Identify corresponding angles and sides of two congruent figures.	Identify all pairs of corresponding sides and angles for the congruent triangles. 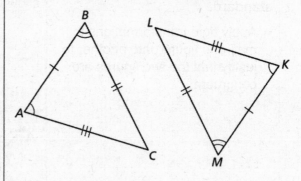

Name_____ Date_____

Geometric Reasoning

H MA.912.GR.2.7 Justify the criteria for triangle congruence using the definition of congruence in terms of rigid transformations.

Circle the scale that best demonstrates your knowledge of the standard.

	Description	Evidence
4	**I can go beyond the standard.** • Teach someone else how to justify the criteria for triangle congruence using the definition of congruence in terms of rigid transformations.	In the diagram, $\angle A \cong \angle D$, $\overline{AC} \cong \overline{DF}$, and $\overline{AB} \cong \overline{DE}$. 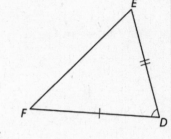 Using rigid motions, explain why $\triangle ABC$ must be congruent to $\triangle DEF$.
3	**I understand the entire standard.** • Justify the criteria for triangle congruence using the definition of congruence in terms of rigid transformations.	In the diagram, $\angle A \cong \angle D$, $\angle B \cong \angle E$, and $\overline{AB} \cong \overline{DE}$. 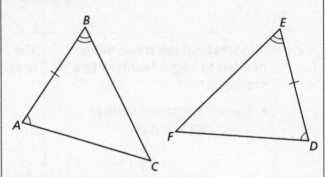 Using rigid motions, explain why $\triangle ABC$ must be congruent to $\triangle DEF$.

MA.912.GR.2.7 (continued)

	Description	**Evidence**
2	**I understand some parts, but not the entire standard.** • Recognize triangle congruence theorems (ASA, SAS, SSS).	Which triangle congruence theorem proves the triangles are congruent? **a.** 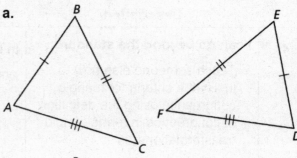 **b.** 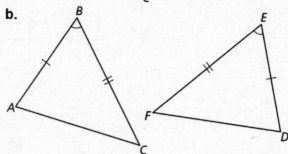 **c.** 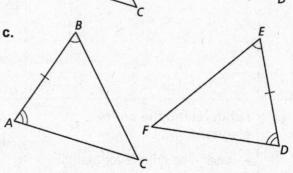
1	**I understand the basic skills needed to begin learning this standard.** • Identify congruent parts of congruent triangles.	The two triangles are congruent. List all the pairs of congruent sides and congruent angles. 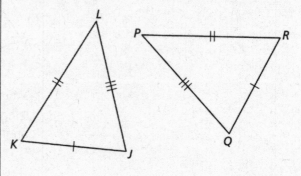

Evidence-Based Scale Worksheets

Geometric Reasoning
MA.912.GR.2.8 Apply an appropriate transformation to map one figure onto another to justify that the two figures are similar.

Circle the scale that best demonstrates your knowledge of the standard.

	Description	Evidence
4	**I can go beyond the standard.** • Write a word problem using transformations to map one figure onto another.	A company logo is designed like the letter V on a rectangular background. The sides of the V form a 48° angle. The width of the rectangle is 1.4 cm, and the height of the rectangle is 2.2 cm. For use on a poster, the logo must be enlarged so that the height is 5.5 cm. **a.** Describe the transformation that will create the desired size logo. **b.** What will be the width of the rectangular background after the transformation? **c.** What will be the measure of the angle formed by the sides of the letter V?
3	**I understand the entire standard.** • Apply an appropriate transformation to map one figure onto another to justify that the two figures are similar	Find a transformation that will justify that $\triangle ABC$ and $\triangle DEF$ are similar. 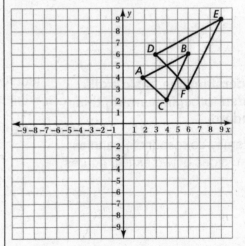

Name_____ Date _____

MA.912.GR.2.8 (continued)

	Description	**Evidence**
2	**I understand some parts, but not the entire standard.** • Find side lengths and angle measures in similar figures.	$\triangle AEC$ is similar to $\triangle BED$. Find each measure. 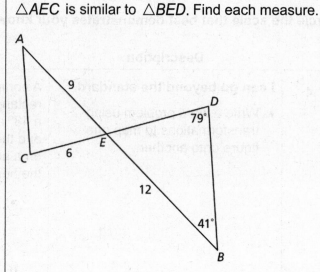 a. $m\angle A$ b. $m\angle C$ c. DE
1	**I understand the basic skills needed to begin learning this standard.** • Identify corresponding angles and sides of two similar figures.	Identify all pairs of corresponding sides and angles for the congruent triangles. 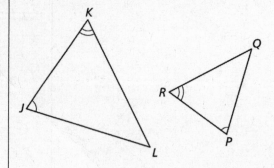

Name_____ Date_____

Geometric Reasoning

H MA.912.GR.2.9 Justify the criteria for triangle similarity using the definition of similarity in terms of non-rigid transformations.

Circle the scale that best demonstrates your knowledge of the standard.

	Description	Evidence
4	**I can go beyond the standard.** • Teach someone else how to justify the criteria for triangle similarity using the definition of similarity in terms of non-rigid transformations.	In the diagram, *DE* = 2*AB*, *DF* = 2*AC*, and $m\angle A \cong \angle D$. 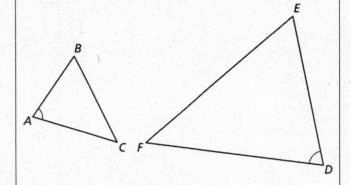 Using transformations, explain why △*ABC* must be similar to △*DEF*.
3	**I understand the entire standard.** • Justify the criteria for triangle similarity using the definition of similarity in terms of non-rigid transformations.	In the diagram, $\angle A \cong \angle D$ and $\angle B \cong \angle E$. 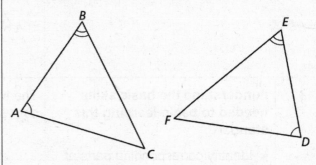 Using transformations, explain why △*ABC* must be similar to △*DEF*.

MA.912.GR.2.9 (continued)

	Description	Evidence
2	**I understand some parts, but not the entire standard.** • Recognize triangle similarity theorems (AA, SAS, SSS).	Which triangle similarity theorem proves the triangles are similar? **a.** 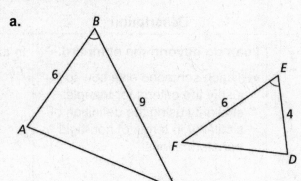 **b.** 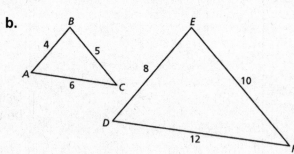 **c.** 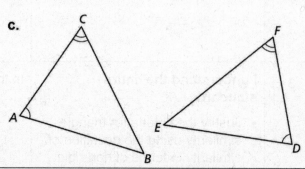
1	**I understand the basic skills needed to begin learning this standard.** • Identify corresponding parts of similar triangles.	The two triangles are similar. List all the pairs of corresponding sides and corresponding angles. 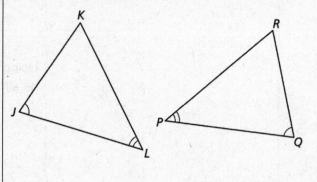

Geometric Reasoning
MA.912.GR.3.1 Determine the weighted average of two or more points on a line.

Circle the scale that best demonstrates your knowledge of the standard.

	Description	Evidence
4	**I can go beyond the standard.** • Solve problems involving the weighted average of two or more points on a line.	Point B has coordinates (-6, -3), point C has coordinates (-4, 1) and point D has coordinates (1, 11). Point C is the weighted average of points B and D. If point D has weight 2, what is the weight of Point B?
3	**I understand the entire standard.** • Determine the weighted average of two or more points on a line.	Point A has coordinates (-2, 5). Point B has coordinates (10, -3). Find the weighted average of A and B if A has weight 3 and B has weight 1.

MA.912.GR.3.1 (continued)

	Description	**Evidence**
2	**I understand some parts, but not the entire standard.** • Find the weighted average of a set of numbers.	Scores for a geometry quiz are shown in the table. | Score	Number of Students
---	---
9	3
8	8
7	12
6	2	 What is the average score on the quiz?
1	**I understand the basic skills needed to begin learning this standard.** • Find the average (arithmetic mean) of a set of numbers.	Find the average (arithmetic mean) of the numbers. 5, 9, 11, 7, 11

Evidence-Based Scale Worksheets

Geometric Reasoning

MA.912.GR.3.2 Given a mathematical or real-world context, use coordinate geometry to classify or justify definitions, properties and theorems involving circles, triangles or quadrilaterals.

Circle the scale that best demonstrates your knowledge of the standard.

	Description	Evidence
4	**I can go beyond the standard.** • Given some points on a geometric figure, use coordinate geometry to find additional points based on geometric properties.	Quadrilateral *DEFG* has coordinates *D*(1, –2), *E*(–1, 2), and *F*(3, 4). Find the coordinates of point *F* so that quadrilateral *DEFG* is a square.
3	**I understand the entire standard.** • Given a mathematical or real-world context, use coordinate geometry to classify or justify definitions, properties and theorems involving circles, triangles or quadrilaterals.	△*ABC* has vertices *A*(–2, –1), *B*(–3, 3), and *C*(2, 0). Classify △*ABC*. Justify your response.

MA.912.GR.3.2 (continued)

	Description	Evidence
2	**I understand some parts, but not the entire standard.** • Use coordinates to find distance, slope and midpoint.	Given the points $A(3, -4)$ and $B(-7, 20)$, find each of the following. **a.** slope of $\overleftrightarrow{AB}$ **b.** the length AB **c.** the midpoint of $\overline{AB}$
1	**I understand the basic skills needed to begin learning this standard.** • Recall the slope, distance and midpoint formulas.	Given the points $A(x_1, y_1)$ and $B(x_2, y_2)$, find each of the following. **a.** slope of $\overleftrightarrow{AB}$ **b.** the length AB **c.** the midpoint of $\overline{AB}$

Evidence-Based Scale Worksheets

Geometric Reasoning
MA.912.GR.3.3 Use coordinate geometry to solve mathematical and real-world geometric problems involving lines, circles, triangles and quadrilaterals.

Circle the scale that best demonstrates your knowledge of the standard.

	Description	Evidence
4	**I can go beyond the standard.** • Teach someone else how to use coordinate geometry to solve mathematical and real-world geometric problems involving lines, circles, triangles and quadrilaterals.	Quadrilateral *ABCD* is a parallelogram. Three vertices are *A*(3, −1), *B*(−2, 1), and *C*(1, 4). Find the coordinates of point *D*.
3	**I understand the entire standard.** • Use coordinate geometry to solve mathematical and real-world geometric problems involving lines, circles, triangles and quadrilaterals.	The points *A*(0, 4) and *B*(2, 0) are the endpoints of the diameter of a circle. Find the equation of the line tangent to the circle passing through point *B*.

MA.912.GR.3.3 (continued)

	Description	Evidence
2	**I understand some parts, but not the entire standard.** • Solve simple problems using slope, distance and midpoint formulas.	Point $B(6, -1)$ is the midpoint of segment $\overline{AC}$. If the coordinates of point A are $A(3, 4)$, what are the coordinates of point C?
1	**I understand the basic skills needed to begin learning this standard.** • Use the slope, midpoint and distance formulas.	Given points $D(-3, 4)$ and $E(5, 7)$. a. What is the slope of the line passing through points D and E? b. What is the distance between points D and E? c. What is the midpoint of the segment $\overline{DE}$?

Evidence-Based Scale Worksheets

Geometric Reasoning

MA.912.GR.3.4 Use coordinate geometry to solve mathematical and real-world problems on the coordinate plane involving perimeter or area of polygons.

Circle the scale that best demonstrates your knowledge of the standard.

	Description	Evidence
4	**I can go beyond the standard.** • Write a word problem using coordinate geometry to find the area or perimeter of polygons.	A farmer plans to fence a triangular pasture. She uses the origin on a coordinate plane to represent one corner of the pasture. The second corner is located 200 yards east and 100 yards south of the origin. The third corner is located 100 yards east and 200 yards north of the origin. **a.** How many yards of fencing will be needed to enclose the pasture? Round to the nearest whole number. **b.** What is the total area of the pasture?
3	**I understand the entire standard.** • Use coordinate geometry to solve mathematical and real-world problems on the coordinate plane involving perimeter or area of polygons.	A triangle has vertices (−3, 3), (0, 5) and (4, 1). **a.** Find the perimeter of the triangle. **b.** Find the area of the triangle.

MA.912.AR.3.4 (continued)

	Description	Evidence
2	**I understand some parts, but not the entire standard.** • Find the area and perimeter of a polygon.	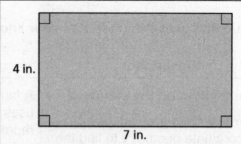 4 in. 7 in. **a.** What is the perimeter of the rectangle? **b.** What is the area of the rectangle?
1	**I understand the basic skills needed to begin learning this standard.** • Use the distance formula to find the distance between two points.	What is the distance between the points (3, 7) and (2, −5)?

Evidence-Based Scale Worksheets

Geometric Reasoning
MA.912.GR.4.1 Identify the shapes of two-dimensional cross-sections of three-dimensional figures.

Circle the scale that best demonstrates your knowledge of the standard.

	Description	Evidence
4	**I can go beyond the standard.** • Teach someone how to identify the shapes of two-dimensional cross-sections of three-dimensional figures	Describe the cross section formed by the intersection of the plane and the solid. 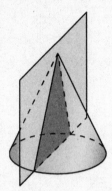
3	**I understand the entire standard.** • Identify the shapes of two-dimensional cross-sections of three-dimensional figures.	Describe the cross section formed by the intersection of the plane and the solid. 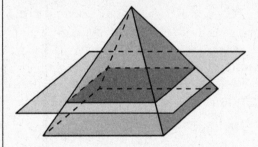

Name _____ Date _____

	Description	Evidence
2	**I understand some parts, but not the entire standard.** • Classify solids	Name each solid. a. 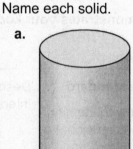 b. 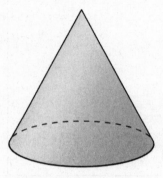 c. 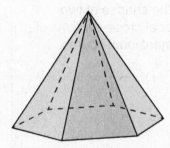
1	**I understand the basic skills needed to begin learning this standard.** • Define cross section.	Define *cross section*.

Name_____ Date_____

Geometric Reasoning
MA.912.GR.4.2 Identify three-dimensional objects generated by rotations of two-dimensional figures.

Circle the scale that best demonstrates your knowledge of the standard.

	Description	Evidence
4	**I can go beyond the standard.** • Teach someone else how to identify three-dimensional objects generated by rotations of two-dimensional figures.	Identify and describe the solid produced by rotating the figure. 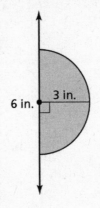 6 in. 3 in.
3	**I understand the entire standard.** • Identify three-dimensional objects generated by rotations of two-dimensional figures.	Identify and describe the solid produced by rotating the figure. 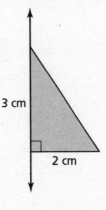 3 cm 2 cm

MA.912.GR.4.2 (continued)

	Description	**Evidence**
2	**I understand some parts, but not the entire standard.** • Recognize solids of revolution.	Identify each solid. **a.**  **b.** 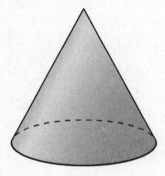 **c.** 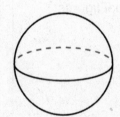
1	**I understand the basic skills needed to begin learning this standard.** • Define axis of revolution.	Define *axis of revolution*.

Name_____ Date_____

Geometric Reasoning
MA.912.GR.4.3 Extend previous understanding of scale drawings and scale factors to determine how dilations affect the area of two-dimensional figures and the surface area or volume of three-dimensional figures.

Circle the scale that best demonstrates your knowledge of the standard.

	Description	Evidence
4	**I can go beyond the standard.** • Write a word problem to determine how dilations affect the area of two dimensional figures and the surface area or volume of three-dimensional figures.	It takes 80 square inches of cardboard to make a box shaped like a rectangular prism. A similar box is constructed using 320 square inches of cardboard. How many times greater is the volume of the second box?
3	**I understand the entire standard.** • Extend previous understanding of scale drawings and scale factors to determine how dilations affect the area of two-dimensional figures and the surface area or volume of three-dimensional figures.	A rectangular prism has a surface area of 52 square inches and a volume of 24 cubic inches. If each edge of the prism is stretched by a scale factor of $\frac{3}{2}$, find the surface area and volume of the transformed prism.

Name _____ Date _____

MA.912.GR.4.3 (continued)

	Description	**Evidence**

2	**I understand some parts, but not the entire standard.**
	
	• Determine how dilations affect the side lengths of two-dimensional figures.
		$\triangle ABC$ is dilated by a scale factor of $\frac{2}{3}$ to form $\triangle DEF$. AB = 12 and EF = 36. Find each of these lengths.
		
		  a. DE
		
		  b. BC

1	**I understand the basic skills needed to begin learning this standard.**
	
	• Define dilation and scale factor.
		Define each of the terms.
		
		  a. dilation
		
		  b. scale factor

Geometric Reasoning
MA.912.GR.4.4 Solve mathematical and real-world problems involving the area of two-dimensional figures.

Circle the scale that best demonstrates your knowledge of the standard.

	Description	Evidence
4	**I can go beyond the standard.** • Solve mathematical and real-world problems involving the volume of three-dimensional figures.	The density of steel is approximately 8 grams per cubic centimeter. What is the weight of a steel sphere with a radius of 3 centimeters?
3	**I understand the entire standard.** • Solve mathematical and real-world problems involving the area of two-dimensional figures.	The downtown neighborhood of a small city is shaped like a square. Each edge measures $\frac{3}{4}$ of a mile. Find the number of people who live downtown if the population density is 5600 people per square mile.

MA.912.GR.4.4 (continued)

	Description	Evidence
2	**I understand some parts, but not the entire standard.** • Find the population density.	Find the population density of a town with a population of 33,900 and a land area of 9.38 square miles.
1	**I understand the basic skills needed to begin learning this standard.** • Define population density.	Define *population density*.

Evidence-Based Scale Worksheets

Geometric Reasoning

MA.912.GR.4.5 Solve mathematical and real-world problems involving the volume of three-dimensional figures limited to cylinders, pyramids, prisms, cones and spheres.

Circle the scale that best demonstrates your knowledge of the standard.

	Description	Evidence
4	**I can go beyond the standard.** • Write a word problem involving the volume of three-dimensional figures limited to cylinders, pyramids, prisms, cones and spheres.	The density of asphalt is 140 pounds per cubic foot. What is the weight of asphalt in a conical pile with a height of 8 feet and a radius of 5 feet?
3	**I understand the entire standard.** • Solve mathematical and real-world problems involving the volume of three-dimensional figures limited to cylinders, pyramids, prisms, cones and spheres.	A cylindrical bucket has a height of 14.5 inches and a diameter of 11 inches. Three gallons of water are poured into the bucket. A gallon contains 231 cubic inches. How many inches is the surface of the water below the top of the bucket?

MA.912.GR.4.5 (continued)

	Description	Evidence
2	**I understand some parts, but not the entire standard.** • Find the volumes of cylinders, pyramids, prisms, cones and spheres.	Find the volume of each figure. **a.** cylinder with a height of 5 centimeters and a radius of 2 centimeters **b.** square pyramid with a height of 5 centimeters and a base area of 6 square centimeters **c.** rectangular prism with edges of 3 centimeters, 5 centimeters and 8 centimeters **d.** right circular cone with a height of 5 centimeters and a radius of 2 centimeters **e.** sphere with a radius of 3 centimeters
1	**I understand the basic skills needed to begin learning this standard.** • Recall the volume formulas.	Write the formula for the volume of each figure. **a.** cylinder **b.** pyramid **c.** prism **d.** cone **e.** sphere

Evidence-Based Scale Worksheets

Geometric Reasoning
MA.912.GR.4.6 Solve mathematical and real-world problems involving the surface area of three-dimensional figures limited to cylinders, pyramids, prisms, cones and spheres.

Circle the scale that best demonstrates your knowledge of the standard.

	Description	Evidence
4	**I can go beyond the standard.** • Write a word problem involving the surface area of three-dimensional figures limited to cylinders, pyramids, prisms, cones and spheres.	A spherical water tank holds 10,000 cubic feet of water. What is the surface area of the tank?
3	**I understand the entire standard.** • Solve mathematical and real-world problems involving the surface area of three-dimensional figures limited to cylinders, pyramids, prisms, cones and spheres.	A propane tank is shaped like a cylinder with a hemisphere on each end. The length of the cylindrical portion is 4 feet, and the radius of the hemispheres and cylinder is 1 foot. Find the surface area of the propane tank.

Name_____ Date _____

MA.912.GR.4.6 (continued)

	Description	Evidence
2	**I understand some parts, but not the entire standard.** • Find the surface area of cylinders, pyramids, prisms, cones and spheres.	Find the surface area of each figure. **a.** cylinder with a height of 5 centimeters and a radius of 2 centimeters **b.** square pyramid with a slant height of 6 centimeters and the length of each edge of the base of 2 centimeters **c.** rectangular prism with edges of 3 centimeters, 5 centimeters and 8 centimeters **d.** right circular cone with a slant height of 6 centimeters and a radius of 2 centimeters **e.** sphere with a radius of 3 centimeters
1	**I understand the basic skills needed to begin learning this standard.** • Recall the surface area formulas.	Write the formula for the surface area of each figure. **a.** cylinder **b.** pyramid **c.** cone **d.** sphere

Name_____   Date_____

Geometric Reasoning
MA.912.GR.5.1 Construct a copy of a segment or an angle.

Circle the scale that best demonstrates your knowledge of the standard.

	Description	Evidence
4	**I can go beyond the standard.** • Teach someone else how to construct a copy of a segment or an angle.	
3	**I understand the entire standard.** • Construct a copy of a segment or an angle.	a. Use a compass and a straightedge to construct a copy of the segment. A•————————————•B b. Use a compass and a straightedge to construct a copy of the angle. 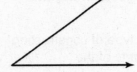

MA.912.GR.5.1 (continued)

	Description	**Evidence**
2	**I understand some parts, but not the entire standard.** • Determine the sequence of steps to copy an angle.	Place the steps to copy an angle in the correct order. a. 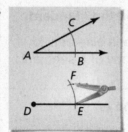 b. 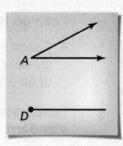 c. 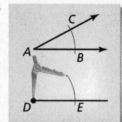 d. 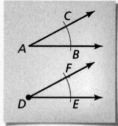
1	**I understand the basic skills needed to begin learning this standard.** • Identify the type of construction given the parts of the construction.	Identify the type of construction given the steps below. 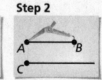 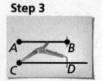

Evidence-Based Scale Worksheets

Geometric Reasoning
MA.912.GR.5.2 Construct the bisector of a segment or an angle, including the perpendicular bisector of a line segment.

Circle the scale that best demonstrates your knowledge of the standard.

	Description	Evidence
4	**I can go beyond the standard.** • Teach someone else how to construct a copy of a segment or an angle.	
3	**I understand the entire standard.** • Construct the bisector of a segment or an angle, including the perpendicular bisector of a line segment.	**a.** Use a compass and a straightedge to construct the perpendicular bisector of the line segment.  **b.** Use a compass and a straightedge to construct the bisector of the angle. 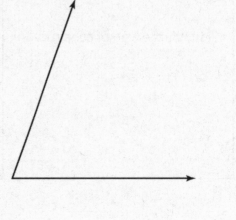

MA.912.GR.5.2 (continued)

	Description	**Evidence**
2	**I understand some parts, but not the entire standard.** • Explain why angles are congruent or segments are congruent in a diagram showing a construction.	Explain why $\angle ABD \cong \angle CBD$ in the following diagram. 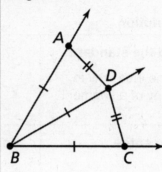
1	**I understand the basic skills needed to begin learning this standard.** • Define the bisector of a segment or an angle.	Define the terms. **a.** angle bisector **b.** segment bisector

Name_____ Date_____

Evidence-Based Scale Worksheets

Geometric Reasoning
MA.912.GR.5.3 Construct the inscribed and circumscribed circles of a triangle.

Circle the scale that best demonstrates your knowledge of the standard.

	Description	Evidence
4	**I can go beyond the standard.** • Teach someone else how to construct the inscribed and circumscribed circles of a triangle.	
3	**I understand the entire standard.** • Construct the inscribed and circumscribed circles of a triangle.	**a.** Using a straightedge, construct a triangle. Then using the straightedge and a compass, construct the inscribed circle of the triangle. **b.** Using a straightedge, construct a triangle. Then using the straightedge and a compass, construct the circumscribed circle of the triangle.

MA.912.GR.5.3 (continued)

	Description	Evidence
2	**I understand some parts, but not the entire standard.** • Determine whether the inscribed or circumscribed circles result from a given construction.	Determine whether the inscribed or the circumscribed circle of a triangle results from each construction. **a.** Construct the perpendicular bisectors of two sides of the triangle. Place the point of the compass at the intersection of the perpendicular bisectors and construct a circle through all three vertices of the triangle. **b.** Construct the angle bisectors of two angles of the triangle. Construct a perpendicular line from the intersection of the angle bisectors through one side of the triangle. Place the point of the compass at the intersection of the angle bisectors and construct a circle passing through the point where the perpendicular line intersects the side of the triangle.

1	**I understand the basic skills needed to begin learning this standard.**
	
	• Define the inscribed and circumscribed circles of a triangle.
		Define the terms.
		
		  a. circumscribed circle
		
		  b. inscribed circle

Evidence-Based Scale Worksheets

Geometric Reasoning

H MA.912.GR.5.4 Construct a regular polygon inscribed in a circle. Regular polygons are limited to triangles, quadrilaterals and hexagons.

Circle the scale that best demonstrates your knowledge of the standard.

	Description	Evidence
4	**I can go beyond the standard.** • Teach someone else how to construct a regular polygon inscribed in a circle.	
3	**I understand the entire standard.** • Construct a regular polygon inscribed in a circle. Regular polygons are limited to triangles, quadrilaterals and hexagons.	Use a compass and straightedge to construct each figure inscribed in a circle. **a.** equilateral triangle 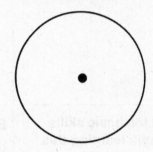 **b.** square 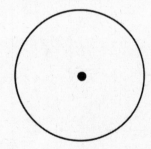 **c.** regular hexagon 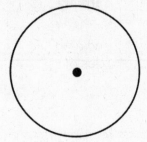

MA.912.GR.5.4 (continued)

	Description	Evidence
2	**I understand some parts, but not the entire standard.** • Determine the sequence of steps in the construction of a geometric figure inscribed in a circle.	Place the steps to construct a square inscribed in a circle in the correct order. Not all steps will be used. **A.** Use the compass to measure the radius. **B.** Connect the endpoints of the diameter to the endpoints of the perpendicular bisector. **C.** Use the center and the straightedge to construct a diameter of the circle. **D.** Make two arcs that intersect the circle at two different points. **E.** Construct the perpendicular bisector of the diameter.
1	**I understand the basic skills needed to begin learning this standard.** • Explain why a step in a construction has a certain property.	Explain why $\overleftrightarrow{CD}$ is the perpendicular bisector of $\overline{AB}$ 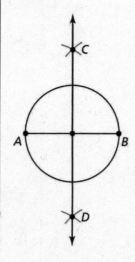

Evidence-Based Scale Worksheets

Geometric Reasoning
Ⓗ **MA.912.GR.5.5** Given a point outside a circle, construct a line tangent to the circle that passes through the given point.

Circle the scale that best demonstrates your knowledge of the standard.

	Description	Evidence
4	**I can go beyond the standard.** • Use the construction of lines tangent to a circle to construct a circumscribed polygon.	Construct a triangle that circumscribes the circle. 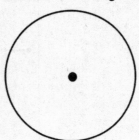
3	**I understand the entire standard.** • Given a point outside a circle, construct a line tangent to the circle that passes through the given point.	Construct a line tangent to the circle from the point. 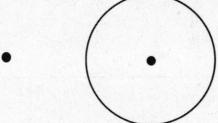

MA.912.GR.5.5 (continued)

	Description	Evidence
2	**I understand some parts, but not the entire standard.** • Construct the perpendicular bisector of a line segment.	Construct the perpendicular bisector of the line segment. •———————————————————•
1	**I understand the basic skills needed to begin learning this standard.** • Define tangent to a circle and perpendicular bisector.	Define the terms. a. tangent to a circle b. perpendicular bisector

Name_____ Date _____

Geometric Reasoning
MA.912.GR.6.1 Solve mathematical and real-world problems involving the length of a secant, tangent, segment or chord in a given circle.

Circle the scale that best demonstrates your knowledge of the standard.

	Description	Evidence
4	**I can go beyond the standard.** • Prove theorems related to the lengths of secant, tangent, segment or chord in a given circle.	Prove that congruent chords of a circle intercept congruent arcs.
3	**I understand the entire standard.** • Solve mathematical and real-world problems involving the length of a secant, tangent, segment or chord in a given circle.	Find the value of x. Explain your reasoning. **a.** 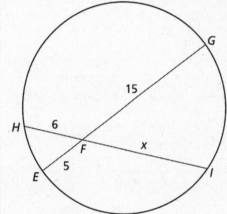 **b.** 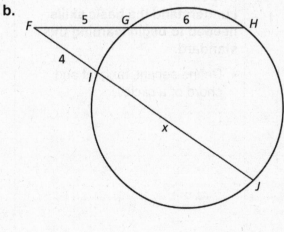

MA.912.GR.6.1 (continued)

	Description	Evidence
2	**I understand some parts, but not the entire standard.** • Identify relationships of secants, tangents and chords of circles.	Match each relationship with one of the diagrams. I 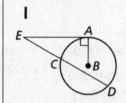 II III **a.** $\overline{AB} \cong \overline{AC}$ **b.** $AB \cdot AC = AD \cdot AE$ **c.** $EA^2 = EC \cdot ED$
1	**I understand the basic skills needed to begin learning this standard.** • Define secant, tangent and chord of a circle.	Define these terms related to circles. **a.** secant **b.** tangent **c.** chord

Evidence-Based Scale Worksheets

Geometric Reasoning
MA.912.GR.6.2 Solve mathematical and real-world problems involving the measures of arcs and related angles.

Circle the scale that best demonstrates your knowledge of the standard.

	Description	Evidence
4	**I can go beyond the standard.** • I can teach someone else how to solve mathematical and real-world problems involving the measures of arcs and related angles.	In the diagram, $\overrightarrow{AB}$ and $\overrightarrow{AC}$ are tangent to circle O. 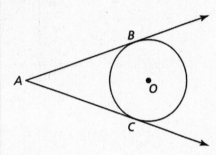 If $m\overparen{BC} = 139°$, what is $m\angle BAC$?
3	**I understand the entire standard.** • Solve mathematical and real-world problems involving the measures of arcs and related angles.	In the diagram, $\overrightarrow{BA}$ is tangent to circle O at point A. 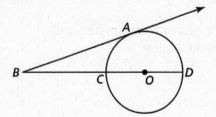 If $m\overparen{AD} = 108°$, what is $m\angle ABD$?

MA.912.GR.6.2 (continued)

Description	Evidence

	Description	Evidence
2	**I understand some parts, but not the entire standard.** • Identify relationships between arcs, inscribed angles and central angles.	Match each relationship with one of the diagrams. I 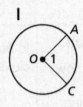 II 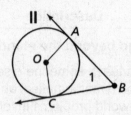 III **a.** $m\angle 1 = \frac{1}{2}m\angle AOC$ **b.** $m\angle 1 = m\overset{\frown}{AC}$ **c.** $m\angle 1 = 180° - m\angle AOC$
1	**I understand the basic skills needed to begin learning this standard.** • Define arcs, central angles and inscribed angles.	Define each term. **a.** arc **b.** central angle **c.** inscribed angle

Evidence-Based Scale Worksheets

Geometric Reasoning
MA.912.GR.6.3 Solve mathematical problems involving triangles and quadrilaterals inscribed in a circle.

Circle the scale that best demonstrates your knowledge of the standard.

	Description	Evidence
4	**I can go beyond the standard.** • Teach someone else to solve mathematical problems involving triangles and quadrilaterals inscribed in a circle.	Find the missing angle measures. 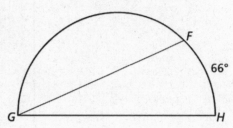
3	**I understand the entire standard.** • Solve mathematical problems involving triangles and quadrilaterals inscribed in a circle.	Find the missing angle measures. 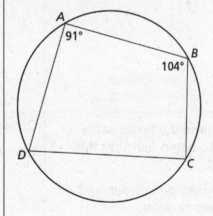

MA.912.GR.6.3 (continued)

	Description	**Evidence**
2	**I understand some parts, but not the entire standard.** • Find missing angle measures in triangles and quadrilaterals.	Find the missing angle measures. **a.** 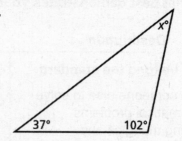 **b.** 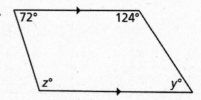
1	**I understand the basic skills needed to begin learning this standard.** • Define inscribed angles and inscribed polygon.	Define each term. **a.** inscribed angle **b.** inscribed polygon

Name_____ Date_____

Geometric Reasoning
MA.912.GR.6.4 Solve mathematical and real-world problems involving the arc length and area of a sector in a given circle.

Circle the scale that best demonstrates your knowledge of the standard.

	Description	Evidence
4	**I can go beyond the standard.** • Write a word problem involving the arc length or area of a sector in a given circle.	Write a word problem involving the arc length or area of a sector of a circle.
3	**I understand the entire standard.** • Solve mathematical and real-world problems involving the arc length and area of a sector in a given circle.	Circle C has radius 6 centimeters, and $m\overset{\frown}{AB} = 50°$. a. Find the length of $\overset{\frown}{AB}$. b. Find the area of the sector bounded by $\overset{\frown}{AB}$ and $\angle ACB$.

Name _____ Date _____

MA.912.GR.6.4 (continued)

	Description	Evidence

Description   Evidence

2   **I understand some parts, but not the entire standard.**

- Find the circumference and area of a circle.

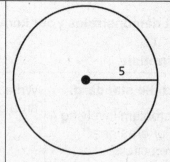

a. Find the circumference of the circle.

b. Find the area of the circle.

1   **I understand the basic skills needed to begin learning this standard.**

- Define arc length and sector of a circle.

Define the terms.

a. arc length

b. sector of a circle

Name_____ Date_____

Geometric Reasoning
Ⓗ **MA.912.GR.6.5** Apply transformations to prove that all circles are similar.

Circle the scale that best demonstrates your knowledge of the standard.

	Description	Evidence
4	**I can go beyond the standard.** • Create a word problem involving similar circles.	Write a word problem involving similar circles.
3	**I understand the entire standard.** • Apply transformations to prove that all circles are similar.	Use transformations to prove that a circle with center *O* and radius *r* is similar to a circle with center *P* and radius *s*.

MA.912.GR.6.5 (continued)

	Description	**Evidence**
2	**I understand some parts, but not the entire standard.** • Apply transformations to circles.	Describe a series of transformations that will map ⊙O onto ⊙P. 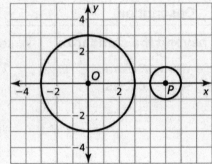
1	**I understand the basic skills needed to begin learning this standard.** • Define similar figures.	Define *similar figures*.

Evidence-Based Scale Worksheets

Geometric Reasoning
MA.912.GR.7.2 Given a mathematical or real-world context, derive and create the equation of a circle using key features.

Circle the scale that best demonstrates your knowledge of the standard.

	Description	Evidence
4	**I can go beyond the standard.** • Derive and create the equation of a circle given enough information to deduce the key features.	The points (1, 7) and (9, 1) are the endpoints of the diameter of a circle. Write the equation of the circle in standard form.
3	**I understand the entire standard.** • Given a mathematical or real-world context, derive and create the equation of a circle using key features.	Write the equation of a circle with center (2, −4) and radius 3.

MA.912.GR.7.2 (continued)

	Description	Evidence
2	**I understand some parts, but not the entire standard.** • Find the center and radius of a circle given its equation in standard form.	The equation of a circle is shown. $$(x - 3)^2 + (y + 5)^2 = 81$$ Find the center and radius of the circle.
1	**I understand the basic skills needed to begin learning this standard.** • Write the equation of a circle centered at the origin.	A circle centered at the point (0, 0) has radius 7. Write the equation of the circle in standard form.

Name_____ Date_____

Geometric Reasoning

MA.912.GR.7.3 Graph and solve mathematical and real-world problems that are modeled with an equation of a circle. Determine and interpret key features in terms of the context.

Circle the scale that best demonstrates your knowledge of the standard.

	Description	Evidence
4	**I can go beyond the standard.** • Write a word problem that could be modeled with an equation of a circle.	Write a word problem that can be modeled with the equation of a circle.
3	**I understand the entire standard.** • Graph and solve mathematical and real-world problems that are modeled with an equation of a circle. Determine and interpret key features in terms of the context.	An irrigation system for a form is in the interior of a circle with equation $$\left(x - 250\right)^2 + (y + 100)^2 = 40{,}000$$ What are the domain and range of the equation?

Name _____ Date _____

MA.912.GR.7.3 (continued)

	Description	Evidence
2	**I understand some parts, but not the entire standard.** • Find the center and radius of a circle from an equation.	What are the center and the radius of the circle with equation $(x + 3)^2 + (y - 7)^2 = 16$?
1	**I understand the basic skills needed to begin learning this standard.** • State the equation of a circle.	Write the equation of a circle with center (h, k) and radius r.

Evidence-Based Scale Worksheets

Trigonometry
MA.912.T.1.1 Define trigonometric ratios for acute angles in right triangles.

Circle the scale that best demonstrates your knowledge of the standard.

	Description	Evidence
4	**I can go beyond the standard.** • Explain the relationships between the three trigonometric ratios for the acute angles in a right triangle.	Explain the relationships between the sine, cosine and tangent ratios for angles *A* and *B*. 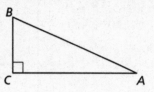
3	**I understand the entire standard.** • Define trigonometric ratios for acute angles in right triangles.	Determine the trigonometric ratios for the given angles. **a.** Find sin *L*, cos *L* and tan *L*. 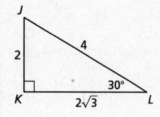 **b.** Find sin *P*, cos *P* and tan *P*. 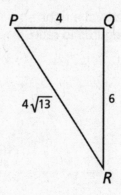

Name _____ Date _____

MA.912.T.1.1 (continued)

	Description	Evidence
2	**I understand some parts, but not the entire standard.** • Identify trigonometry ratios of acute angles in a right triangle.	For each ratio, name the correct trigonometry function. Assume the triangle is a right triangle. **a.** $\dfrac{\text{adjacent}}{\text{hypotenuse}}$ **b.** $\dfrac{\text{opposite}}{\text{adjacent}}$ **c.** $\dfrac{\text{opposite}}{\text{hypotenuse}}$
1	**I understand the basic skills needed to begin learning this standard.** • Identify the parts of a right triangle with regards to ratio.	Identify each side as *adjacent, opposite or hypotenuse* with regards to ∠A. 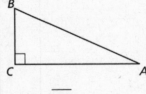 **a.** $\overline{AB}$ **b.** $\overline{BC}$ **c.** $\overline{AC}$

Evidence-Based Scale Worksheets

Trigonometry

MA.912.T.1.2 Solve mathematical and real-world problems involving right triangles using trigonometric ratios and the Pythagorean Theorem.

Circle the scale that best demonstrates your knowledge of the standard.

	Description	**Evidence**
4	**I can go beyond the standard.** • Create a real-world problem using trigonometry ratios and the Pythagorean Theorem to solve right triangles.	
3	**I understand the entire standard.** • Use trigonometry ratios and the Pythagorean Theorem to solve real-world problems involving right triangles.	The top of a slide is 15 feet from the ground and has an angle of depression of 46°. **a.** What is the length of the slide? Round your answer to the nearest hundredth of a foot. **b.** How far is the bottom of the slide to the bottom of the ladder of the slide? Round your answer to the nearest hundredth of a foot.

Name _____ Date _____

	Description	**Evidence**
2	**I understand some parts, but not the entire standard.** • Use trigonometry ratios and the Pythagorean Theorem to solve mathematical problems involving right triangles.	Find the value of x, y and z in the diagram. 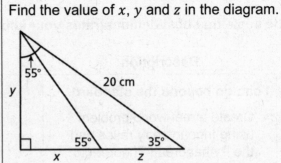
1	**I understand the basic skills needed to begin learning this standard.** • Find the length of the hypotenuse of a right triangle.	Find the length of the hypotenuse. 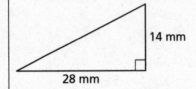

Name_____ Date _____

Trigonometry

Ⓗ **MA.912.T.1.3** Apply the Law of Sines and the Law of Cosines to solve mathematical and real-world problems involving triangles.

Circle the scale that best demonstrates your knowledge of the standard.

	Description	Evidence
4	**I can go beyond the standard.** • Explain what given information is needed to use the Laws of Sines and Cosines. Explain when there are no possible or two possible triangles based on the given information.	Explain what given information is needed to use the Laws of Sines and Cosines. Explain when there are no possible or two possible triangles based on the given information.
3	**I understand the entire standard.** • Apply the Law of Sines and the Law of Cosines to solve real-world problems involving triangles.	**a.** Two rangers are 10 miles apart when they see the start of a forest fire. Ranger A's sight line with the road is 36°. Ranger B's sight line with the road is 47°. How far is each ranger from the fire? **b.** Two sides of a triangular plot of land are 750 feet and 650 feet. The angle between the sides is 123°. What is the perimeter of the triangular plot of land to the nearest ten feet?

MA.912.T.1.3 (continued)

	Description	**Evidence**

2	**I understand some parts, but not the entire standard.**
	
	• Apply the Law of Sines and the Law of Cosines to solve mathematical problems involving triangles.
		Find the missing side(s) and angle(s) of the triangle. Round your answers to the nearest hundredth.
		
		   a. $a = 14, c = 12, A = 35°$
		
		   b. $a = 10, b = 7, C = 48°$

1	**I understand the basic skills needed to begin learning this standard.**
	
	• Solve problems involving the Pythagorean Theorem.
		Find the missing side of the right triangle. Round your answers to the nearest tenth, if necessary.
		
		   a. The legs are 8 centimeters and 12 centimeters. What is the length of the hypotenuse?
		
		   b. The length of one leg is 24 inches and the length of the hypotenuse is 25 inches. What is the length of the other leg?

Name_____ Date _____

Trigonometry
Ⓗ **MA.912.T.1.4** Solve mathematical problems involving finding the area of a triangle given two sides and the included angle.

Circle the scale that best demonstrates your knowledge of the standard.

	Description	Evidence
4	**I can go beyond the standard.** • Solve a real-world problem involving finding the area of a triangle given two sides and the included angle.	A triangular garden is built in a community. Two sides of the garden are 45 feet and 36 feet. The angle between the two sides is 71°. What is the area of the garden to the nearest tenth of a foot?
3	**I understand the entire standard.** • Solve mathematical problems involving finding the area of a triangle given two sides and the included angle.	Find the area of each triangle to the nearest tenth. **a.** The length of the two sides are 12 inches and 16 inches. The included angle is 48°. **b.** The length of the two sides are 5 centimeters and 8 centimeters. The included angle is 116°.

MA.912.T.1.4 (continued)

	Description	**Evidence**
2	**I understand some parts, but not the entire standard.** • Determine if the area of a triangle can be found based on the given information.	Determine if the area of a triangle can be found based on the given information. **a.** $a = 21, c = 16, A = 48°$ **b.** $a = 10, c = 32, C = 71°$ **c.** $a = 5, b = 8, c = 12$
1	**I understand the basic skills needed to begin learning this standard.** • Find the area of triangles.	Find the exact area of each triangle. **a.** An equilateral triangle with a side length of 6 centimeters. **b.** An isosceles right triangle with a hypotenuse of 10 inches.

Evidence-Based Scale Worksheets

Logic and Discrete Theory

MA.912.LT.4.3 Identify and accurately interpret "if...then," "if and only if," "all" and "not" statements. Find the converse, inverse and contrapositive of a statement.

Circle the scale that best demonstrates your knowledge of the standard.

	Description	Evidence
4	**I can go beyond the standard.** • Create conditional statements and write the corresponding converse, inverse and contrapositive statements. Explain and defend the validity of each statement.	Create your own "if . . . then" statement and write the converse, inverse and contrapositive. Determine if the statements are true or false.
3	**I understand the entire standard.** • Find the converse, inverse and contrapositive statements, and accurately interpret the statements.	Write each statement. Determine if the statements are true or false. A square is a rectangle. **a.** Conditional statement **b.** Converse **c.** Inverse **d.** Contrapositive

MA.912.LT.4.3 (continued)

	Description	Evidence
2	**I understand some parts, but not the entire standard.** • Identify notation used for conditional, converse, inverse and contrapositive statements.	Identify the notation for each statement. **a.** Conditional statement **b.** Converse **c.** Inverse **d.** Contrapositive
1	**I understand the basic skills needed to begin learning this standard.** • Write conditional statements.	Write a conditional statement for each sentence. **a.** When I ride a bicycle, I wear a helmet. **b.** I live in the state of Florida, which is in the United States.

Logic and Discrete Theory
H MA.912.LT.4.8 Construct proofs, including proofs by contradiction.

Circle the scale that best demonstrates your knowledge of the standard.

	Description	Evidence
4	**I can go beyond the standard.** • Teach someone else the steps required to construct a proof by contradiction.	
3	**I understand the entire standard.** • Construct proofs by contradiction.	Prove the following statement using proof by contradiction. In an isosceles triangle, base angles are congruent.

Name _____ Date _____

MA.912.LT.4.8 (continued)

	Description	Evidence
2	**I understand some parts, but not the entire standard.** • Determine the steps necessary for constructing proofs by contradiction.	Make a plan of how to construct a proof by contradiction. If x is odd and y is even, then xy is even.
1	**I understand the basic skills needed to begin learning this standard.** • Write contradictions for statements.	Write a contradiction for each statement. **a.** In $\triangle XYZ$, if $\angle X$ is a right angle, then the other angles are acute. **b.** If x is an integer and x^2 is odd, then x is odd.

314 **Florida Geometry**
B.E.S.T. Test Prep and Practice Workbook

Copyright © Big Ideas Learning, LLC
All rights reserved.

Name_____ Date_____

Logic and Discrete Theory
MA.912.LT.4.10 Judge the validity of arguments and give counterexamples to disprove statements.

Circle the scale that best demonstrates your knowledge of the standard.

	Description	Evidence
4	**I can go beyond the standard.** • Create a mathematical statement that may appear to be always true. Provide at least one counterexample to make the statement false. Rewrite the statement to make it true.	
3	**I understand the entire standard.** • Judge the validity of arguments and give counterexamples to disprove statements.	Give a counterexample for each statement. Rewrite each statement to make it always true. **a.** For three collinear points, *A*, *B*, and *C* then $AB + BC = AC$. **b.** For a regular polygon, the exterior angles are acute.

MA.912.LT.4.10 (continued)

	Description	Evidence
2	**I understand some parts, but not the entire standard.** • Provide counterexamples to disprove statements.	Give a counterexample to disprove the statement. **a.** Multiplying a whole number by a fraction results in a smaller number. **b.** All quadrilaterals with two pairs of congruent sides are parallelograms.
1	**I understand the basic skills needed to begin learning this standard.** • Identify statements as true or false.	Determine if each statement is true or false. **a.** A quadrilateral with four congruent sides is a square. **b.** An isosceles triangle is also an acute triangle. **c.** A regular polygon has all interior angles that are congruent and all sides that are congruent.